D1241939

THEOPHRASTUS
DE LAPIDIBUS

THEOPHRASTUS

DE LAPIDIBUS

EDITED WITH INTRODUCTION,

TRANSLATION AND COMMENTARY

BY

D. E. EICHHOLZ

PROFESSOR OF CLASSICS
UNIVERSITY OF BRISTOL

OXFORD

AT THE CLARENDON PRESS

1965

Oxford University Press, Amen House, London E.C.4

GLASGOW NEW YORK TORONTO MELBOURNE WELLINGTON
BOMBAY CALCUTTA MADRAS KARACHI LAHORE DACCA
CAPE TOWN SALISBURY NAIROBI IBADAN
KUALA LUMPUR HONG KONG

© *Oxford University Press 1965*

PRINTED IN GREAT BRITAIN

549
T394d
161152

PREFACE

I offer this volume as a small tribute to the memory of Dr. Stanley Smith, F.G.S., sometime Reader in Palaeontology in the University of Bristol, who in 1942 proposed to me that we should together produce an edition of Theophrastus' treatise *On Stones*. It was agreed that he would be responsible for Part II of the edition, a series of mineralogical chapters, while my own task would be to edit and translate the text, and to provide a textual commentary and introductory chapters. When Dr. Smith died in 1955, the project was by no means complete. In 1956 an edition was published in the U.S.A. by Earle R. Caley and John F. C. Richards, also a product of long collaboration. Although this edition contains much that is of value, I did not feel that it rendered superfluous the work on which Dr. Smith and I had been engaged. I therefore completed both parts of the work, his and mine. However, it has not been found possible to publish what was intended to be Part II. The present volume represents my share of the work, with virtually no modifications except that short mineralogical notes have been added to the textual commentary in order to make the volume independent of the unpublished portion.

These mineralogical notes would have been beyond my capacity but for the many discussions I had with Dr. Smith during his lifetime. I am also grateful for the help offered more recently by colleagues and other experts in various scientific fields. Among these I am especially indebted to Professor F. Coles Phillips and Dr. F. H. Pollard of the University of Bristol, and to Mr. Robert H. S. Robertson. In my collation of the Greek manuscripts I owe much to the kindness of Professor John F. C. Richards, who suggested that I should use his photographs of nine manuscripts that were discovered after his own edition had been published. Published and unpublished information provided by Mr. Nigel G. Wilson has been of great service in dating the manuscripts. I have to thank the editors and publishers of the *Classical Quarterly* for allowing me to republish my article on Aristotle's theory of the formation of metals and minerals, and the trustees of the Colston Research Fund for meeting the cost of preparing photographed copies of the textual apparatus. I must express my gratitude to the Publications Committee of the University of Bristol for its generosity in providing a subvention for the publication of this book.

D. E. E.

Bristol,
April, 1964

CONTENTS

INTRODUCTION

THEOPHRASTUS AND SOME CHARACTERISTICS OF THE *DE LAPIDIBUS*

O U R information concerning the life of Theophrastus is derived mainly from Diogenes Laertius, *Lives and Opinions of Famous Philosophers*, v. 36–57. Many details are uncertain.[1]

Theophrastus was born between 372 and 370 B.C. at Eresos in the island of Lesbos, his father being Melantas, a fuller. The tradition that his original name was Tyrtamus and that he was renamed Theophrastus by Aristotle owing to the excellence of his style is of doubtful authenticity. Theophrastus received his early education at Eresos. It is uncertain when he first met Aristotle. If we can accept the tradition that he studied philosophy under Plato, they would have met as fellow-students in the Academy before 348 or 347 B.C., for in one or the other of these years Plato died. However, Theophrastus was probably a member of Aristotle's circle as early as 344, when Aristotle moved from Assos in Asia Minor to Lesbos and settled at Mytilene, not far from Theophrastus' birthplace. In 343–342 Theophrastus accompanied Aristotle to the Macedonian court, and later to Stagira in Chalcidike,[2] where they stayed until Aristotle's pupil Alexander came to the throne of Macedon. Theophrastus again accompanied Aristotle on his return to Athens in 335–334 and helped him to establish the Peripatetic School in the Lyceum. Aristotle died in 321. In the previous year he had been threatened with a prosecution for impiety and had retired to Chalcis, leaving Theophrastus to succeed him as head of the School. This office he held until his death in 288–286. The *De Lapidibus* was written in or shortly after 315–314 (see pp. 8–12).

Athenaeus (i. 21a–b) has preserved a vivid picture of Theophrastus as his audience must have seen him in his prime: 'According to Hermippus, Theophrastus would appear at a regular

[1] For all questions concerning Theophrastus, see the article 'Theophrastus' by O. Regenbogen in Pauly–Wissowa, *Real-Encyclopädie*, Suppl. VII, published in 1940. This includes a note on the *De Lapidibus* (cols. 1415–16). The article 'Peripatos' by K. O. Brink in the same volume throws much light on the setting in which Theophrastus worked.

[2] See W. Jaeger, *Aristoteles* (Berlin, 1923), p. 116, n. 1.

hour in the School, well groomed and elegantly dressed. He would then take his seat and deliver his lecture, using freely every kind of gesture and pose. Once, while he was giving an imitation of an epicure he stuck out his tongue and licked his lips voluptuously.'

Like Aristotle, Theophrastus incurred suspicion at Athens because of his friendship with the rulers of Macedon. Not long before he wrote the *De Lapidibus*, he was accused of impiety, but was triumphantly acquitted. For ten years or so until 307 he enjoyed the favour of Demetrius of Phalerum, his pupil, who during this period controlled Athens on behalf of the regent of Macedon, Cassander. When Demetrius fell, Theophrastus, along with other philosophers, was exiled under the terms of the Decree of Sophocles, but returned in the following year, 305, when the decree was declared invalid. These setbacks did no permanent damage to his standing in the community, and when he died all the citizens are said to have attended his funeral as a mark of respect. He appears to have been fully worthy of their esteem. His helpfulness was well known (εὐεργετικός, Diog. Laert. v. 36), and his dislike of snobbery, arrogance, and pretentiousness, which is a conspicuous feature of the *Characters*, his most famous work, must have endeared him to the common man.

As a philosopher, he was extraordinarily industrious (φιλοπονώτατος, Diog. Laert. v. 37), and in scope his writings are comparable only with those of Aristotle himself.[1]

The Peripatetic School was intended by Aristotle to perform the functions which we associate with a university. It provided instruction and undertook research in a wide range of humane and scientific studies, logic, metaphysics, the natural sciences, political science, ethics, and literary theory. Aristotle himself welded these studies into a vast, comprehensive system of 'philosophy'. But this system was not regarded either by him or by his pupils as a final statement of doctrine. In all its branches it was treated as a basis for further discussion and inquiry, and Aristotle's most gifted disciples felt that they could live most truly in the spirit of their master by striving to develop and perfect it.

---

[1] There is a list of his writings in Diog. Laert. v. 42–50. Of these there survive the *Characters*, the two great botanical works (the *History of Plants* and the *Causes of Plants*), and a number of shorter studies, of which the *De Lapidibus* is one.

None of Aristotle's successors addressed himself more whole-heartedly to this task than Theophrastus. In his researches he covered almost the whole ambit of Aristotle's studies. Much of his work consisted of monographs like the *De Lapidibus*, and in this he reflects a tendency towards specialization which was characteristic of the age, but was even more clearly marked in his successors, each of whom appears to have been a specialist in one field. Theophrastus himself resisted this tendency. To judge from the *De Lapidibus*, his monographs were self-contained studies, but not isolated studies.

The relation of the De Lapidibus to other works of Theophrastus. The *De Lapidibus* was a companion study to the *De Metallis* (§ 1) and was accompanied by other studies in the same field, one on *Petrifactions* (Diog. Laert. v. 42; cf. §§ 4, 38), one on the *Sicilian Lava-flow* (Diog. Laert. v. 49; cf. § 22), and one on *Salt, Nitre, and Alum* (Diog. Laert. v. 42). These four works have not survived, but the connexion is obvious. The *De Lapidibus* was also connected with works lying outside the field of mineralogy. Thus the long digression on combustible stones in §§ 9–22 encroaches upon the subject of the *De Igne*, which itself returns the compliment (*De Igne*, § 46). Finally there must have been a close link between the *De Lapidibus* and works of a more general character, such as one on *Separation* (περὶ ἐκκρίσεως, Diog. Laert. v. 46), another on *Solidification and Dissolution* (περὶ πήξεων καὶ τήξεων, Diog. Laert. v. 45), and another on *Heat and Cold* (Diog. Laert. v. 44), which must have dealt fully with the concepts alluded to in §§ 2 and 3.

At the same time, the *De Lapidibus* is closely related to certain works of Aristotle. Theophrastus' purpose in general was to continue the work of his teacher, and the treatise is conceived with this end in view.

Theophrastus' dependence upon Aristotle. In the last chapter of Book iii of the *Meteorologica* (*Mete.* 378ª19 ff.), Aristotle gives a brief and general account of the formation of minerals and metals,[1] and at the end of the chapter promises a more detailed study. This promise was never carried out by Aristotle: Book iv of the *Meteorologica* is concerned with other matters. The omission was made good by Theophrastus, as Aristotle's commentators, Alexander

---

[1] For a discussion, see pp. 38 ff.

of Aphrodisias and Olympiodorus, are careful to point out. One
of the treatises which he wrote for this purpose, the *De Metallis*,
is lost. The other is the *De Lapidibus*.

Thus Aristotle's chapter in the *Meteorologica* is the starting-
point of the *De Lapidibus*, and his remarks provide a foundation
for Theophrastus' own theory of the formation of stones and
mineral earths. Hence the distinction drawn in § 1 between metals
as watery substances and stones and mineral earths as earthy
substances roughly corresponds to the distinction made by Aristotle between metals and 'fossiles'. Again, in § 3 Theophrastus
accepts the principle laid down in *Meteorologica* Book iv that,
where solidification is due to heat, dissolution must be due to
cold, and vice versa.[1] Even the concepts of 'filtering' ($\delta\iota\dot{\eta}\theta\eta\sigma\iota\varsigma$)
and of the 'conflux' ($\sigma\upsilon\rho\rho\sigma\dot{\eta}$) which he introduces in § 2 can be
discerned in Aristotle's explanation of certain physiological pro-
cesses (see p. 27, n. 2).

Theophrastus' dependence on Aristotle must not, however, be
exaggerated. His attitude to Aristotle is objective and sometimes,
at least by implication, critical. This is clear from the fragments
and notices of his lost works and is seen unmistakably in such
works as the *Metaphysica*.

Criticism of Aristotle. So, too, the opening statement of the *De
Lapidibus*, that stones are earthy substances, probably contains an
implicit criticism of *Meteorologica* Book iv, where it is maintained
that some stones are composed of water (*Mete.* 389ᵃ8–9).[2] Again,
he avoids using the term $\tau\dot{\alpha}$ $\dot{\sigma}\rho\upsilon\kappa\tau\dot{\alpha}$ ('things dug', 'fossiles'),
whereby Aristotle had distinguished minerals from metals ($\tau\dot{\alpha}$
$\mu\epsilon\tau\alpha\lambda\lambda\epsilon\upsilon\dot{\sigma}\mu\epsilon\nu\alpha$). He no doubt felt that Aristotle's terminology
was misleading and arbitrary because minerals no less than metals
are mined (and are thus $\mu\epsilon\tau\alpha\lambda\lambda\epsilon\upsilon\dot{\sigma}\mu\epsilon\nu\sigma\iota$, § 39), while many stones
that are *not* minerals are dug ($\dot{\sigma}\rho\upsilon\kappa\tau\sigma\dot{\iota}$). Hence he extends his
use of the words $\mu\epsilon\tau\alpha\lambda\lambda\epsilon\upsilon\dot{\sigma}\mu\epsilon\nu\sigma\varsigma$ and $\mu\epsilon\tau\alpha\lambda\lambda\epsilon\upsilon\tau\dot{\sigma}\varsigma$ (§§ 9, 39) from
metals to minerals and tends to restrict $\dot{\sigma}\rho\upsilon\kappa\tau\dot{\sigma}\varsigma$ to non-mineral
substances (§§ 29, 37, 42; but cf. § 48). Finally, there is direct
criticism of Aristotle in § 40, where Theophrastus contradicts the

---

[1] It is safer to write 'laid down in *Meteorologica* Book iv' than 'laid down by
Aristotle' since his authorship of this book has been questioned: see p. 18, n. 4.
However, there must be many things in this book that are Aristotelian, and there
is no reason to doubt that this principle is one of them.

[2] See footnote 1, above. This doctrine too is likely to be Aristotelian. Theophrastus seems to criticize other details in *Meteorologica* Book iv: see p. 18, n. 4.

opinion expressed in the last chapter of *Meteorologica* Book iii that all mineral earths are coloured powder (see p. 47).

But the difference between the two philosophers is far more deeply rooted than a bare divergence of opinion on this or that topic would suggest. In Theophrastus we are confronted with a different type of mind. His interest was centred upon the concrete rather than upon the abstract, and the energy which he devoted to the collection, examination, and marshalling of facts was inexhaustible. As compared with Aristotle, he attaches a far higher value to facts and the evidence to be derived from observing facts, and at the same time shows far less readiness to pursue general questions and proceed to general conclusions. Both of these tendencies can be detected in the *De Lapidibus*.

The importance of collecting and observing facts. A large part of the *De Lapidibus* is taken up with the description of various kinds of stones and earths. Theophrastus collects his information from many regions. In the course of his survey he ranges from Scythia to Aswan and from Spain to Bactria. What is especially notable is the wealth of detail derived from regions which had been brought within the frontiers of the Greek world by the conquests of Alexander the Great. Cappadocia, Cilicia, Syria,[1] Phoenicia, Armenia, the Persian Gulf, and in particular Egypt yield new and valuable information. In this respect, the *De Lapidibus*, like the two treatises on plants, is a characteristic product of the age.

Like them also, it is characteristic of its author in the stress which it lays upon the observation of facts. Although Theophrastus obviously enjoyed collecting facts for their own sake, he did not forget that his facts had been collected in order to be examined. Hence the occurrence of phrases such as μαρτυρεῖν δὲ οἱ τόποι δοκοῦσιν (§ 20), σημεῖον δὲ λαμβάνουσιν ὅτι . . . (§ 21), πλείους ἄν τις λάβοι τὰς ἰδιότητας (§ 40), and μαρτυρεῖ δ' ἡ γένεσις αὐτή (§ 54). Accordingly, in supporting Aristotle's opinion that certain mineral earths are produced by the dry exhalation, it is natural for him to include an appeal to visual evidence (καὶ ἔνιά γε δὴ φαίνεται πεπυρωμένα, § 50).

Reluctance to make generalizations. The collection and study of numerous facts impressed Theophrastus with a lively sense of their diversity. This, superimposed on the keen analytical faculty

---

[1] From Syria Theophrastus received the first reasonable information about the nature of glass to reach Greece (see p. 36, n. 2).

which we see engaged in works such as the *De Sensu et Sensibilibus*
and the *Metaphysica*, produced in him an attitude of extreme
caution. Consequently, just as διαφορά ('difference', 'distinctive
characteristic') is a term which pervades his expositions, so
σχεδόν ('just about', 'approximately') is a word that qualifies his
statements so frequently as to become a linguistic mannerism.

The manner in which the careful observation of facts leads
Theophrastus to non-committal conclusions can be seen clearly
in §§ 20–21, where the subject under discussion is the formation of
pumice. Theophrastus first mentions the view that all pumice,
except that formed of sea-foam, is produced by combustion.
There is, he states, evidence for this view to be found both in
pumice itself and in the places from which it comes. But some
pumice, that of Nisyros, appears to be formed of sand; and for
this too there is apparently reliable evidence. Accordingly, he
suggests that 'it is possible that, while some pumice is formed
under such conditions, some is formed differently and that there
are several ways in which it is generated'. Similarly cautious pro-
nouncements are made in §§ 2, 3, and 9.[1]

Theophrastus' cautious temper and respect for facts militated
against the confident formulation of theories. It is significant that
in § 29 he makes no attempt to explain the attraction of the
lodestone, an abstract problem which exercised many of the best
Greek minds. It is equally significant that he does explain the
working of the touchstone, which can be readily deduced by
observation (§§ 45, 47).

By far the most important theory stated in the *De Lapidibus* is
that which deals with the formation of stones and earths in §§ 2
and 3, and here no more than a bare summary is presented to us.
If, as seems possible, the *De Lapidibus* originally contained a full
exposition of this theory (see p. 15), Theophrastus cannot in this
instance be accused of shirking the discussion of a theoretical
problem. But it is equally possible that he was unwilling to

---

[1] Another facet of this attitude is the scepticism which Theophrastus brings to
bear on his facts. This, however, is not applied consistently. He is justifiably
sceptical in his view of the effects of the eagle-stone (§ 5) and in his tacit rejection
of the usual ideas about the origin of amber (§ 29). As opposed to this, there are
times when he is caught off his guard, as for example when he admits the possibility that some pumice is formed of sea-foam (§§ 19, 22) and again when he
accepts the popular notions about the origin of the *lyngurium*, where perhaps he was
influenced by the eminent physician, Diocles (§ 28).

record views which he regarded as provisional and as suitable only for the lecture-room. If this is the correct explanation of the omission, his reluctance would be typical of the man.[1] In any case, he shows an obvious reluctance to proceed further in applying the theory to specific instances than is absolutely necessary. His references to it in §§ 50 and 61 are perfunctory and cryptic.

The influence of the 'De Lapidibus'. From the third century B.C. onwards mineralogy was rarely studied by classical writers for its own sake. The earths were treated largely as a branch of pharmacology. Theophrastus, however, mentions the medical properties of no earths, and of only one stone, when he notes that the 'smaragdus' is good for the eyes (§ 24).[2]

The study of stones was focused upon precious and semiprecious gems, and here particular attention was paid to their magical properties. Theophrastus alludes to such properties only once, and then with scepticism (§ 5; the eagle-stone). But as early as the beginning of the third century Sotacus was writing on stones in a spirit utterly alien to that of Theophrastus. His was a spirit that fitted the temper of an age that was losing its faith in rationalism, and he had numerous successors. Some of these took pieces of information from the *De Lapidibus* and transmitted them to the elder Pliny.[3] Thus the *De Lapidibus* was valued as a source of facts, but its influence as a model for further study was negligible.

The theory sketched in the introductory sections had little interest for classical writers.[4] Even the Arabic scientists,[5] whose

[1] O. Regenbogen in Pauly–Wissowa, Suppl. VII, cols. 1419, 1557, observes Theophrastus' unwillingness to pursue the theoretical introduction of the *De Igne* to its conclusions, in spite of the important consequences involved. The same writer (*Hermes*, lxix (1934), 97) notices similar marks of incompleteness in Book i of the *Historia Plantarum*.

[2] Similarly, he excluded pharmacology from his treatises on plants.

[3] For these developments, see Max Wellmann, 'Die Stein- und Gemmenbücher der Antike' (*Quellen und Studien zur Geschichte der Naturwissenschaften und der Medizin*, iv, pt. 4, Berlin, 1935, pp. 86 ff.). Wellmann thinks that Pliny derived most of his quotations of the *De Lapidibus* from intermediate sources.

[4] The Stoics may have been an exception. There is evidence that Posidonius pursued such speculations (see Pliny, *Natural History*, vol. x, Loeb Classical Library, Books xxxvi–xxxvii, trans. D. E. Eichholz, pp. x–xv).

[5] For instance, Avicenna (see E. J. Holmyard and D. C. Mandeville, *Avicennae de Congelatione et Conglutinatione Lapidum*, Paris, 1927) and the Brothers of Purity (see F. Dieterici, *Die Philosophie der Araber im IX. und X. Jahrhundert n. Chr.*, vol. v, *die Naturanschauung und Naturphilosophie*, Leipzig, 1876, pp. 95 ff.).

speculations owed something to the *Meteorologica*[1] of Aristotle, neglected it.[2] This is understandable. The exposition is too cautious, prosaic, brief, and above all obscure to lend itself to development. The first and only serious attempt to understand Theophrastus' theory came with the Renaissance. Its author was Georgius Agricola,[3] who thanks to his knowledge of mining and mineralogy gained an insight into the nature and value of Theophrastus' ideas and incorporated them in a theory of his own.

THE DATE OF COMPOSITION

In § 59 it is stated that Callias, an Athenian, discovered how to produce artificial cinnabar 'about ninety years before the archonship of Praxibulus at Athens' (περὶ ἔτη μάλιστ' ἐνενήκοντα εἰς ἄρχοντα Πραξίβουλον Ἀθήνῃσι). Praxibulus was archon in 315–314 B.C.[4] Consequently the *De Lapidibus* could not have been written before 315–314 B.C., and it has sometimes been assumed that the work was composed in these very years.[5]

This assumption was attacked by W. Jaeger in his book, *Diokles von Karystos*, published in 1938. Jaeger attempted to link evidence from the *De Lapidibus* with the controversial question of the date of Diocles' death, which he placed after 300 B.C. His arguments (op. cit., pp. 116–33) may be summarized as follows:

(1) Pp. 116–19. The Diocles referred to in § 28 is Diocles of Carystus. The use of the imperfect tense in this reference ('as Diocles used to say', ὥσπερ καὶ Διοκλῆς ἔλεγεν) indicates that Diocles was no longer alive when the *De Lapidibus* was written.

---

[1] See, for example, Holmyard and Mandeville, op. cit., p. 35, footnote.

[2] F. de Mély, in his treatise *Les Lapidaires de l'antiquité et du Moyen Age*, vol. iii, pp. xli–xlvi, makes a desperate attempt to prove that a number of Theophrastus' concepts are reproduced by Avicenna, but fails to do so. Only one simple point need be mentioned. De Mély (p. xliii) identifies ἀπολίθωσις in *De Lap.*, § 60, with Avicenna's 'vis mineralis lapidificativa quae congelat aquas'. But ἀπολίθωσις in the passage mentioned has nothing to do with water; it refers to the hardening of earths (presumably clays) into stony matter. Holmyard and Mandeville interpret the congelation of water into stones as the deposition of solids from water. If this interpretation is correct, it is just conceivable that Avicenna borrowed the idea from Theophrastus, whose συρροή performs a similar function (see pp. 23–25).

[3] See p. 47 and n. 1.

[4] Ol. 116. 2. See Diodorus Siculus xix. 55. 1.

[5] For instance Schneider, *Theophrasti Eresii Opera*, vol. iv, p. 585; E. Zeller, *Aristotle and the Earlier Peripatetics*, vol. ii, p. 378, n. 6; and Christ–Schmid, *Griechische Literatur*, 6th ed., vol. ii, pt. 1, p. 63, n. 2.

Having committed himself to this interpretation, Jaeger was forced to find further arguments to support the view that the *De Lapidibus* was written not in or about 315 B.C., but after 300 B.C.

(2) Pp. 123–33. He therefore maintained that this late date was confirmed by the references to the records (ἀναγραφαί) of the Egyptian kings in §§ 24 and 55. In his opinion it was unlikely that a student was sent from the Lyceum to study the records. On the contrary, Theophrastus must have made use of a literary work in which the records were turned to account. The work in question would be the Egyptian history of Hecataeus of Abdera, which was published not earlier than 305 B.C., the year in which Ptolemy assumed the title of King.

(3) Pp. 119–23. Above all, Jaeger discounted the evidence of § 59 on the grounds that Theophrastus was here using a literary source in which he found the archonship of Praxibulus cited as the date at which the manufacture of cinnabar at Laurium had ceased.

Thus, according to Jaeger's thesis, the *De Lapidibus* must have been written at least fifteen years after 315 B.C.

All of his arguments are invalid:

(1) Shortly after the publication of his book, Jaeger himself abandoned the view that the use of the imperfect tense in § 28 must mean that Diocles was already dead. In an article published in the same year,[1] he maintained merely that Diocles was no longer living in Athens when Theophrastus wrote the *De Lapidibus*. This equally plausible interpretation Jaeger had already discussed in his book, only to reject it as unlikely. Therefore, there is no longer any reason to suppose that there is a connexion between § 28 and the date of Diocles' death.

The abandonment of this argument, however, does not in itself impair the two supporting arguments, and these must be considered on their own merits:

(2) The references to the records of the Egyptian kings do not

[1] 'Vergessene Fragmente des Peripatetikers Diokles von Karystos', *Abh. der Preussischen Akademie der Wissenschaften*, 1938, Phil.-hist. Klasse, no. 3, pp. 17 ff. This change of front was necessary because Jaeger had previously overlooked a detail which now forced him to conclude that Diocles was still alive in 270 B.C., several years after the death of Theophrastus. Thus he could no longer allow the *De Lapidibus* to have a bearing on the date of Diocles' death.

Both the book and the article were reviewed by L. Edelman in the *American Journal of Philology*, lxi (1940), 483–9.

appear to justify the conclusions drawn by Jaeger from their presence. In particular, his contention that the material was not collected by a student from the Lyceum, but was derived after 305 B.C. from the writings of Hecataeus of Abdera, is arbitrary. It is possible that no student was involved, but there were others, travellers and resident correspondents, who no doubt provided material for the *De Lapidibus*,[1] as they did for the botanical works. Jaeger himself mentions (p. 127) that the priests were in the habit of translating the records to visitors,[2] so that it is difficult to understand why he should have insisted that Theophrastus was forced to make use of a literary source, and particularly of Hecataeus. It is probable that he would not have stressed this argument had he not been anxious, and indeed over-anxious, to prove in his book that Diocles was still alive after 300 B.C.

(3) Jaeger's attempt to discredit the evidence of § 59 is hardly more successful. According to him, Theophrastus was here using a literary source and found the archonship of Praxibulus mentioned there because it was in 315 B.C. that the production of cinnabar at Laurium came to an end.

The latter suggestion may be dismissed at once. Theophrastus does not even hint that cinnabar was produced at Laurium, nor is there the slightest evidence here or elsewhere that this was ever the case. Indeed, Theophrastus makes it clear that it was only after migrating to Ionia that Callias discovered near Ephesus the sand which, he hoped, would yield gold, but which actually proved to be the raw material of artificial cinnabar.

Nor is there any evidence to show that the date was adopted from another source. On the contrary, the formula appears elsewhere in Theophrastus' writings expressed in terms so similar as to suggest immediately that he himself was responsible for devising it. For in *H.P.* 6. 3. 3 he mentions that the settlement of Cyrene dates back 'about three hundred years before the archonship of Simonides at Athens' (310–309 B.C.).[3] We may compare

---

[1] See, for instance, the description of the search for the Bactrian stones (§ 35), which was probably contributed by a member of Alexander's suite.

[2] Diodorus Siculus (i. 46. 7–8) in a passage quoted by Jaeger (pp. 130–1) mentions the numerous visitors who came to Egypt in the time of Ptolemy I. No doubt the influx started soon after Alexander's conquest. The note on the use of 'poros' in Egyptian buildings (§ 7) would appear to come from an eye-witness.

[3] This passage refutes Hill's rendering of § 59, which would place the invention of artificial cinnabar ninety years *after* Praxibulus' archonship, instead of ninety

this phrase, μάλιστα περὶ τριακόσια (sc. ἔτη) εἰς Σιμωνίδην ἄρχοντα Ἀθήνησιν, with περὶ ἔτη μάλιστ᾽ ἐνενήκοντα εἰς ἄρχοντα
Πραξίβουλον Ἀθήνησι. Two features call for special notice:
    (a) In both passages, Theophrastus stresses the fact that the
numbers are merely approximate by writing μάλιστα and περί,
'about 300 years', 'about 90 years'. He is anxious to disclaim any
knowledge of the exact date of the founding of Cyrene or of
Callias' discovery. Consequently in estimating the date of Callias'
discovery he would not have materially improved his chronology
had he chosen as his lower limit the archonship of 316–315 or
that of 314–313. Thus there is a strong presumption that the
archonship of 315–314 B.C. was chosen not to secure accuracy,
since accuracy was in the nature of the case impossible, but
because 315–314 B.C. was the time at which the *De Lapidibus*
was written. A strong presumption, however, is not proof positive, and it must be admitted that it is impossible to *prove* that the
De Lapidibus was written in 315–314 B.C. and at no other time.
Nevertheless, it is possible to prove that the date of its composition
falls within ten years of that time. Here we must consider a second
feature which is common to both passages:
    (b) In both passages the formula is a convenient approxima-
tion; but it is convenient because it is expressed in *round numbers*.
In the *Historia Plantarum* the period is calculated in terms of
centuries (300 years), in the *De Lapidibus* of decades (90 years).
Now 'ninety years' is admittedly a convenient expression, but
'one hundred years' is a more natural one. Why, then, did not
Theophrastus write 'about one hundred years before the archonship of Euxenippus at Athens' (in 305–304 B.C.)? Doubtless
because at the time when he wrote the archonship of Euxenippus
was still to come. Consequently the date of composition must fall
between the years 315 and 305 B.C. The archonship of Praxibulus
does not, as Jaeger and others have supposed, merely provide
a *terminus post quem*. It can also be used with certainty to fix the
latest possible date of composition.
    Thus, in spite of Jaeger's attempts at disproof, 315–314 B.C. is
still the most probable date of composition, and it can be stated

years *before* it. L. Thorndike, in an essay on disputed dates, &c., in Theophrastus
(*Essays on the History of Medicine*, ed. Charles Singer and Henry E. Sigerist, London,
1924, pp. 74–75) is mistakenly inclined to follow Hill's version and make 225–224
B.C. the date of the *De Lapidibus*. See the Commentary ad loc.

with certainty that the *De Lapidibus* was written between 315 and 305 B.C.

Both Schneider and Wimmer regard the *De Lapidibus* in its extant form as the relic of a larger work. Schneider sees in it a series of excerpts,[1] while Wimmer for his part considers it to be a fragment, for in both his editions it is labelled 'Fragmentum II'. Neither Schneider nor Wimmer explains his view, a serious omission because each view has different implications.

The term 'fragment' suggests a work which has lost its opening or closing sections, or both. This does not appear to be true of the *De Lapidibus*. On the other hand, it seems possible that details are missing from the body of the work. These omissions, if they were numerous, might conceivably lead to the conclusion that the *De Lapidibus*, as we have it, is a series of excerpts.

An examination of the opening and closing sections will show that the *De Lapidibus* is not a fragment in any strict sense of the word. We can then consider to what extent the work seems to have been impaired by internal omissions, and whether these are to be ascribed to an epitomizer.

A. *Is the 'De Lapidibus' a Fragment?*

1. There is no reason to suspect the loss of any sections preceding the present § 1. For this section introduces, appropriately enough, the fundamental distinction between water, as the constituent of metals, and earth, as the constituent of the stones and the earths to be discussed in the course of the book. Moreover, the first sentence lacks a connecting particle, as is so often the case at the beginning of Theophrastus' works. We may compare the *Historia Plantarum*, *De Causis Plantarum*, *De Igne*, *De Odoribus*, *De Ventis*, and *De Signis Tempestatum*.

2. Again, nothing appears to have vanished from the end of the *De Lapidibus*. It is true that our text ends somewhat abruptly with an account of gypsum, but there is good reason to suppose that gypsum was the last item on Theophrastus' list. For in § 61

---

[1] Schneider's notes (vol. iv, pp. 535 ff.) are headed 'Ad Excerpta Libri De Lapidibus'. Again (p. 566), our attention is drawn to details which may have been omitted 'ab excerptore Theophrasti'.

he writes that 'there still remain (ἔτι λοιπά) those (kinds of earths) that are found in earth-pits', thus clearly implying that these are the last of the earths that he intends to discuss. Of these earths he mentions in § 62 'three or four natural earths which are useful as well as unusual, namely the Melian, the Cimolian, the Samian, and finally besides these the Tymphaic, otherwise known as "gypsum" '. Thereupon he deals with the Melian and Samian earths in some detail, omits the familiar Cimolian or fullers' earth, and finally discusses gypsum, the last of the four, at suffi- cient length to make it unlikely that he had more to add. Nor would he have had occasion to refer to yet other *stones*. In § 48, where the transition from stones to earths has taken place, Theophrastus has already made it clear that his dissertation on stones is complete (αἱ μὲν οὖν τῶν λίθων διαφοραὶ καὶ δυνάμεις σχεδόν εἰσιν ἐν τούτοις. αἱ δὲ τῆς γῆς, κτλ.).

Hence the *De Lapidibus* is not a fragment in the sense that it lacks its original opening or closing paragraphs, or both. The treatise always began where it now begins, for nothing could have preceded the present § 1. And there can be little doubt that the present ending is the original ending, since it bears every appearance of completing Theophrastus' last topic.

B. *Is the 'De Lapidibus' a Series of Excerpts?*

1. In §§ 2 and 3 the description of the processes whereby stones and earths are formed is so concise as to be cryptic. It is not sur- prising, therefore, to find in § 2 an allusion to a previous state- ment on the matter (ὡς ἀνωτέρω εἴρηται). Such a statement does not occur in our text. Moreover, in § 50 (ὥσπερ ἐξ ἀρχῆς εἴπομεν) and in § 61 (ὥσπερ ἐλέχθη κατ' ἀρχάς), there are other references to details that should have found a place close to the beginning of the book in a fuller discussion of the processes of formation. Consequently there is apparently a considerable hiatus between the present § 1 and the present § 2.

Such a hiatus, however, may well have been due to Theophras- tus himself. Here, as elsewhere in his introductions, Theophrastus may have failed to edit his notes adequately because he hesitated to commit himself to theories which he regarded as partly pro- visional (see p. 7, n. 1, and p. 15, n. 2).

2. Athenaeus (iii. 93a–b) quotes from § 36 of the *De Lapidibus*

an extract concerning the pearl.[1] It is noteworthy that this, the only quotation in Athenaeus from the *De Lapidibus*, ends with a remark which is missing from the extant text, but is probably authentic (see the Commentary ad loc.). With this crucial instance before us, it is hard to resist the suspicion that there may be other omissions in the text. But such a suspicion can hardly be made the basis of an argument. In itself, the omission preserved by Athenaeus suggests a faulty transmission of our text rather than the mutilation of the text by an epitomizer; and, indeed, similar signs of a faulty transmission have been traced elsewhere in Theophrastus' writings.[2]

It should be mentioned that among the many quotations from Theophrastus that occur in the mineralogical books (xxxi–xxxvii) of Pliny's *Natural History* not one can be traced to a missing passage of the *De Lapidibus*. There are seven passages in which Theophrastus is cited, but which are not derived from extant passages of the *De Lapidibus*. Of these, four (xxxi. 13–14, 17, 19, 26) refer to water, and must come from the lost work 'On Waters' (περὶ ὑδάτων). Two others (xxxi. 83, 106) are concerned with salt and nitre respectively, and must belong to the lost work 'On Salt, Nitre, and Alum' (περὶ ἁλῶν, νίτρου, στυπτηρίας). The seventh passage (xxxvi. 134) is somewhat more complicated. Here Pliny writes: 'idem Theophrastus et Mucianus esse aliquos lapides qui pariant credunt; Theophrastus et ebur fossile candido et nigro colore inueniri et ossa e terra nasci inuenirique lapides osseos.' Theophrastus mentions stones 'that give birth' (οἱ τίκτοντες) in § 5 of the *De Lapidibus*, and 'fossil' ivory with black and white markings in § 37. But the final phrase has no counterpart in the extant text. The 'bone-like stones', however, would have been a suitable topic for the lost work 'On Petrifactions' (περὶ τῶν ἀπολιθουμένων);[3] and the 'bones that grow from the earth' would have been as much in place there as in the *De Lapidibus*.

Pliny includes one other detail that might appear at first sight

---

[1] Part of the extract is quoted also by Clement of Alexandria (*Paedag.* ii. 13).

[2] Otto Regenbogen ('Theophrast-Studien' I. 2, *Hermes*, lxix (1934), 202) finds evidence of considerable wastage in a major work, the *Historia Plantarum*. The wastage, however, appears to be confined to certain books, and thus does not suggest the work of an epitomizer. Regenbogen concludes that Theophrastus' esoteric works were at one period exposed to 'serious damage' (*schwere Schädigung*).

[3] To this work or to the monograph 'On Fishes that Live on Dry Land' (fr. 171, Wimmer) must belong *De Odoribus*, § 37, a misplaced sentence referring to sea-creatures found inside split stones.

to come from a missing passage in the *De Lapidibus*. This is his statement (xxxvii. 65) that the Bactrian 'smaragdus' is found in the joints of rocks (*in commissuris saxorum*). No such statement exists in the corresponding passage of the *De Lapidibus* (§ 34). But Salmasius (*Plinianae Exercitationes*, 139a 8) was clearly right in suggesting that Pliny has here mistranslated εἰς τὰ λιθοκόλλητα. For although he has obviously attempted a close paraphrase, he has not recorded Theophrastus' comment on the use of the Bactrian stones in inlay-work, to which the mistranslated phrase refers. Thus there are no traces of lost portions of the *De Lapidibus* to be found in Pliny.

To sum up, the existing text of the *De Lapidibus* lacks at least one remark. At the same time, there is no evidence of omissions so numerous as to justify us in regarding our text as a series of excerpts. Finally, even if there are omissions that are unknown to us, they are not likely to be extensive. For the *De Lapidibus*, which Diogenes Laertius (v. 44) describes as a treatise in one book only, must have been a short work from the outset.

THE FORMATION OF EARTHS AND STONES
ACCORDING TO THEOPHRASTUS

In its extant form the introduction to the *De Lapidibus* (§§ 1–3) provides merely a sketch of the processes whereby Theophrastus conceived the formation of stones and earths as taking place. He gives no more than a simple statement (ὡς ἁπλῶς εἰπεῖν, § 2). It is possible, however, that the introduction, as it was originally composed, contained a much fuller exposition of this important theme. For in the course of the treatise there occur no less than three allusions to statements which are now lacking, but which must have formed part of the original introduction.[1] One of these allusions actually occurs in § 2 of the present introduction. From this we may conclude that there is a hiatus between § 1 and the extant § 2, and that § 2 and, in all probability, § 3 are merely a recapitulation of a more detailed account which existed at least in Theophrastus' mind,[2] if not in writing.

---

[1] In § 2 (ὡς ἀνωτέρω εἴρηται), § 50 (ὥσπερ ἐξ ἀρχῆς εἴπομεν), and § 61 (ὥσπερ ἐλέχθη κατ᾽ ἀρχάς).

[2] See pp. 10–11. We cannot exclude the possibility that the *De Lapidibus* consists of lecture notes, some of which were not adequately expanded for publication. O. Regenbogen, 'Theophrast-Studien', *Hermes*, xlix (1934), 79–80, sees signs of

The evidence provided by this recapitulation is too meagre to allow of anything like a complete reconstruction of Theophrastus' theory. Nevertheless some conclusions can be drawn with confidence. If others are more questionable, it should be remembered that Theophrastus himself is sometimes content to keep an open mind.[1]

The process of formation set forth in the introduction may be divided for the purposes of discussion into three parts:

A. Of those substances which are formed underground, stones and (mined) earths are of earth, while metals are of water (§ 1).

B. This earth becomes a pure and uniform matter, as the result either of a 'conflux' (συρροή) or of 'filtering' (διήθη-σις) or of some other process of 'separation' (ἐκκρίνεσθαι) (§ 2).

C. This pure, uniform matter, when subjected to heat or cold, undergoes 'hardening', 'solidification' (πῆξις), and forms stones and (mined) earths (§ 3).

A. *The Primary Constituents*

The proposition that stones and mined earths are derived from earth is so obvious as to be almost a tautology.[2] On the other hand, the assertion that metals are derived from water appears to be arbitrary.

Theophrastus did not invent either theory. Plato in the *Timaeus* (59a–b) had already maintained that metals were formed of

inadequate editing in the introduction to the *Historia Plantarum*. It is not at all likely that ὡς ἀνωτέρω εἴρηται refers to the lost *De Metallis* and that the missing introduction dealing with the formation of earths and stones occurred at the beginning of this work. For just previously Theophrastus has referred to it as *another* treatise (ἐν ἄλλοις, § 1).

[1] See, for instance, § 3 (there is nothing to prevent some kinds of stone from being formed either by heat or by cold), § 5 (scepticism regarding the eagle-stone), § 21 (it is possible that pumice may be formed in several ways). Regenbogen's treatment of the problem (Pauly–Wissowa, *Real-Encyclopädie*, Suppl. VII, cols. 1417–18) is puzzling and disappointing.

[2] But it was less obvious to the Greeks than to us. Because κρύσταλλος means both 'ice' and 'rock-crystal', the common Greek view was that rock-crystal, like ice, was formed from water; and this view was seriously maintained long after Theophrastus' time. See Strabo ii. 3. 4, Seneca, *Nat. Quaest.* iii. 25. 12, Pliny xxxvii. 23, Diodorus ii. 52. 1–2. Similarly 'many *nameless* stones are of water' (Aristotle, *Mete.* 389ᵃ8–9). It is possible that Theophrastus made a limited concession to the common view in the case of gemstones. See pp. 36–37.

water, while stones and earths were formed of particles of earth. Similarly Aristotle (*Mete.* 378ª19 ff.; see pp. 38–47) distinguished between 'fossils', which are stones and mineral earths and are formed by the action of the dry exhalation, and metals, which have as their original material the moist exhalation.

The reason which led both Plato and Aristotle to suppose that water, or rather some watery substance, was the primary constituent of metals is not hard to discover.

Plato (loc. cit.) expounds the formation of metals as follows: 'Of all those kinds of water which we have termed "*fusible*", one that is very dense, consisting as it does of very fine, uniform particles, a unique kind, tinged with a shining, yellow hue, is gold.' The other metals are likewise formed from 'fusible varieties of water'.

Aristotle (*Mete.* 378ª26 ff.) was clearly influenced by Plato: 'All metals, those substances which are either *fusible* or *malleable*, such as iron, copper, gold, are products of the vaporous exhalation.' It is obvious that what led both Plato and Aristotle to suppose that the metals are formed from water or some form of water was the fact that they melt or (as in the case of iron) become malleable when subjected to heat.

Neither Plato nor Aristotle derives the metals from water such as is ordinarily known to us. Plato's water is in this instance a special fusible variety. That of Aristotle is strictly speaking not water at all, but an exhalation secreted from the moisture on and within the earth owing to the heat generated by the sun. It was once potentially water, but is so no longer (p. 41). Theophrastus, however, in § 1 states merely that the metals 'are of water'. Did he then reject Aristotle's view? This seems unlikely because the part which he assigns to the *dry* exhalation in the formation of certain earths appears to be substantially the same as assigned to it by Aristotle in the formation of 'fossils' (pp. 46–47). Consequently Theophrastus' use of the term 'water' in this passage must not be taken literally. We are not to suppose that the metals are composed of water, but merely of something which, as Aristotle says (*Mete.* 378ª33–34), 'might have become water, but can do so no longer'.

This conclusion forces us to raise a vital question. If the metals are not, strictly speaking, composed of water, in what sense are the stones and earths composed of earth? What is meant by 'earth' in this context? Is it used loosely for the dry exhalation, just as 'water' in the same sentence is used loosely for the moist exhalation? This suggestion may be rejected. For although Aristotle regarded the moist exhalation as the material cause of the metals, it seems clear that he did not regard the dry exhalation as the material cause of stones and earths, but as the efficient cause of some of them; and Theophrastus appears to have taken the same view (see pp. 43–47).[1] Consequently, stones and mineral earths are composed not of the dry exhalation, but of earth. Or more precisely, of the four 'so-called elements'[2] or 'apparently simple bodies'[3]—Earth, Water, Air, and Fire—Earth is the primary constituent of stones and mineral earths. Earth, however, is their main constituent, and not their only one, since another 'so-called element', Water, must enter into their composition, as with all determinate bodies, if they are to cohere. For there is no reason to suppose that Theophrastus differed from Aristotle on this point.[4] In § 8 of the *De Igne* he states that 'earth

---

[1] F. Solmsen, *Aristotle's System of the Physical World*, Cornell, 1960, p. 401, n. 38, refers to the article reprinted in this volume on pp. 38–47, and doubts whether its author has succeeded in showing that the dry exhalation is the efficient rather than the material cause of the 'fossiles'. It is regrettable that Aristotle's statement (*Mete.* 378ᵃ21–26) is so concise; but Theophrastus indicates clearly enough that the dry exhalation is the efficient cause (see pp. 46–47, where the important passage from *De Lap.* 50 is discussed). With the phrase ἀπὸ τῆς ἀναθυμιάσεως (*De Lap.* 50) we may compare ἡ κίσηρις ἐκ κατακαύσεως ('from combustion') δοκεῖ τισι γίνεσθαι (§ 19), where ἐκ similarly cannot refer to anything but an efficient cause.

[2] Aristotle, *De Partibus Animalium*, 646ᵃ13.

[3] Aristotle, *De Generatione et Corruptione*, 330ᵇ2.

[4] The relevant statements in Aristotle's works are the following:

(a) *Mete.* 388ᵃ13 ff. Stone is a 'homeomerous' (uniform) body; that is, it is divisible into parts each of which is similar in character to any other part and to the whole. (The same is true of metals; of flesh, sinews, bones, &c., in animals; and of wood, bark, leaves, and roots in plants.)

(b) *De Partibus Animalium* 646ᵃ13 ff. The components of 'homeomerous' bodies are the 'so-called elements', Earth, Water, Air, and Fire.

(c) *Mete.* 382ᵃ2 ff. Of the elements Earth is especially representative of the Dry, and Water of the Moist; and therefore all determinate bodies contain both Earth and Water.
    For:

(d) *Mete.* 381ᵇ29 ff., both must be present in all determinate bodies since the Moist is what makes them determinable. Hence

(e) *De Caelo* 302ᵇ15 ff., stones belong to that class of 'homeomerous' bodies that are 'mixed bodies'.

Three of these passages, (a), (c), and (d), belong to *Meteorologica* Book iv. Since this book has been held to be spurious, we may recall that Aristotle himself seems to refer to it both in the *De Partibus Animalium* (649ᵃ33 ff.) and in the *De Generatione Animalium* (784ᵇ7 ff.). [continued on p. 19]

will not cohere if moisture is entirely and utterly lacking'.[1] In this passage 'earth' is the element, and the statement must include all things of which earth is an ingredient, stones as well as earths. It is true that in § 11 of the *De Lapidibus* we hear of stones that 'dry up completely' through exposure to the sun, while in § 19 pumice and cinders are said to be fireproof 'because they contain no moisture'. But 'completely' and 'no moisture' must

Mrs. I. Hammer-Jensen (*Hermes*, l (1915), 121–30) advanced the theory that the youthful Strato was the author of the book, but her arguments have been refuted by I. Düring (*Aristotle's Chemical Treatise Meteorologica Book iv*, Göteborg, 1944, pp. 18–19, 106), who concludes that 'this treatise as to language and doctrines perfectly agrees with what we know to be genuinely Aristotelian'. See also H. D. P. Lee, Aristotle, *Meteorologica* (Loeb Classical Library, Harvard, 1952), introduction, pp. xiii–xxi.

F. Solmsen in his review of Lee's edition (*Gnomon*, xxix (1957), 153) once more contests the authenticity of *Meteorologica* iv. For example, he regards 384^{b}30 ff. as a clumsy attempt to harmonize *Meteorologica* iv with the last chapter of *Meteorologica* iii. The passage in question does in fact make sense, although it is open to misinterpretation (see p. 46). No one would deny the point that Solmsen makes with emphasis in his book, *Aristotle's System of the Physical World*, p. 402, namely that the programme announced at the end of *Meteorologica* iii is not carried out in *Meteorologica* iv. It was, however, continued by Theophrastus (see pp. 3–4), who incidentally criticized details both from the last chapter of *Meteorologica* iii (see p. 47) and from *Meteorologica* iv (see below). In the present volume Aristotle is cited as the author of *Meteorologica* iv, although on occasion the reader is reminded that his authorship has been questioned. Whoever the author may have been, there can be no doubt that certain of the theories propounded in *Meteorologica* iv were of fundamental importance to Theophrastus. For example, his notes on solidification and dissolution in § 3 cannot be understood apart from them (see pp. 28–29). More recently H. B. Gottschalk (*Classical Quarterly*, N.S., xi (1961), 67–79) has brought a formidable array of arguments against Aristotle's authorship of *Meteorologica* iv. He suggests that the book is 'a thorough revision of an Aristotelian work by a pupil of Theophrastus using the results of his researches into chemistry and mineralogy' (loc. cit., p. 78). This is most improbable. Gottschalk has not observed, for example, (1) that Theophrastus' note on 'pyromachi' and millstones in § 9 drastically corrects the account of these stones given in *Mete.* 383^{b}5 ff. (see pp. 31–32); or (2) that Theophrastus in § 29 discards by implication the traditional version of the origin of amber given in *Mete.* 388^{b}21, and replaces it by one that is still incorrect, but less fanciful (see § 29 and the Commentary); or that (3) Theophrastus' guarded description of glass as being composed of an earth (§ 49) is an advance on *Mete.* 389^{a}8–9, where glass is stated to be composed of water. That Theophrastus is indebted to *Meteorologica* iv is undeniable. Apart from the doctrines regarding the Dry and the Moist, and Solidification and Dissolution, which have been mentioned above, it is possible, as Gottschalk points out, that Theophrastus took from it the theory of 'pores'. In support of this Gottschalk (p. 73) quotes *De Igne* 42, but the theory may well underlie also the remarks on 'adamas' in *De Lap.* 19 (see the Commentary). Whatever its authorship may be, there is much justification for using *Meteorologica* iv as a means of elucidating Theophrastus.

[1] ἡ δ' (sc. γῆ) οὐκ ἂν συμμείνειεν ἀπολιπόντος πάντη καὶ πάντως τοῦ ὑγροῦ.

be over-statements. In neither case can moisture be 'entirely and utterly lacking'.[1]

B. The Second Stage of Formation

Earth, then, is the element which predominates in stones and mineral earths. But it could not give rise to them in its natural state since in this state it could not impart to them certain of the qualities which many of them possess, for example smoothness, solidity, lustre, and transparency[2] (τὸ λεῖον καὶ τὸ πυκνὸν καὶ τὸ στιλπνὸν καὶ διαφανές, § 2). Theophrastus accounts for qualities such as these by the fact that what forms stones and mineral earths is not earth in its natural state, but earth which has previously become 'a pure and uniform matter' (§ 2).[3]

This pure, uniform matter is produced either by a 'conflux' (συρροή) or by 'filtering' (διήθησις) or by some other method of separation (εἴτε . . . κατ' ἄλλον τρόπον ἐκκεκριμένης, § 2), and we have next to consider how the two former processes were envisaged. Our conclusion will be that the essential difference between the products of these two processes lies not in their quality, but in the form in which they occur.

Filtering. The idea that 'filtering' plays a part in mineralogy appears, like the idea that metals are formed of water, to originate with Plato. In the *Timaeus* 59a–b, a passage already quoted in part (p. 17), he describes gold as a very dense variety of 'fusible' water, 'which has been *filtered*[4] through rock and has there been hardened'. Whether other metals besides gold are similarly compacted by being filtered through rock is not stated; no alternative, however, is suggested.

Stones similarly are shown by Plato to be formed by 'filtering' (*Timaeus* 60b–c):

Of earths, there is one which by being *filtered*[5] through water becomes

---

[1] Aristotle makes similar over-statements. See p. 33, n. 1.

[2] It seems clear from the inclusion of transparency in the list that the process of formation outlined by Theophrastus applies to rock-crystals and other gemstones, as well as to non-precious stones. See p. 16, n. 2.

[3] This does not mean that the *same kind* of pure, uniform matter gives rise to all stones and minerals earths. It must differ with each species. Theophrastus himself implies in § 2 (ὅσῳ ἂν . . . ὑπάρχει) that it possesses purity and uniformity in varying degrees. Compare also § 61, καθαρωτέρας καὶ ὁμαλωτέρας τῶν ἄλλων, of the earths dug in earth-pits.

[4] ἠθημένος. Cf. Theophrastus' term διήθησις.

[5] ἠθημένον.

a stony mass in the following manner. When the water that mixes with it is broken up during the mixing, it is transformed into air, and having become air rises quickly to its own region. But since there was no empty space surrounding it, it thrusts itself against the neighbouring air. This air is heavy; so that when it receives the thrust and is poured round the mass of earth, it squeezes the mass with great force and presses it together into the places from which the new air rose. Earth pressed together so as to be insoluble in water forms stone, the finer stone being transparent because it is composed of equal and uniform particles, and the inferior the reverse.

The theory, in so far as it bears upon the present discussion, may be summarized thus: gold is formed of water which has been compacted by percolating *through rock*: stones (the precious stones included) are formed of earth which has been compacted as the result of being *filtered through water*. The function which 'filtering' performs in Plato's theory is clearly quite different from that assigned to it by Theophrastus. For Plato, its function is not to supply pure matter, but to solidify matter, the purity of which depends on the uniformity of the component 'particles'. In other words, Plato associates 'filtering' with the part which Theophrastus assigns to heat and cold: it belongs to the final, not to the penultimate stage of formation.

Nevertheless Plato's use of the idea is instructive, for he would hardly have introduced it had he not believed that it explained some important fact. And what he presumably had in mind was the fact that gold normally occurs in *veins* enclosed by hard rock.[1] We are to infer that the percolation of the 'fusible' water through narrow passages in the rock and its congelation in these passages will bring about the characteristic formation of gold in subterranean veins.

It must be admitted that the analogous formation of stones as the result of the filtering of earth through water appears to offer no such correspondence with the facts of nature.[2] Here the

[1] See A. E. Taylor, *Commentary on Plato's Timaeus*, p. 416 (note on 59ᵇ4): 'The suggestion is that the narrowness of the passage through the unyielding rock (quartz?), hinted at by the expression that it is "strained" or "filtered" through, forces the particles of the molten metal close together and so effects solidification in the fashion just described.' This theory would have needed some modification in order to account for the formation of metals other than gold, since these, unlike gold, occur in metalliferous ores. Plato was no doubt aware of this complication, but chose to ignore it.

[2] See, however, p. 26, n. 4.

temptation to make the two parts of the theory engagingly sym-
metrical has led Plato into strange paths. But it should be remembered that he himself warns us against treating his suggestions as
if they were a considered doctrine.[1]

Theophrastus was acquainted with the *Timaeus*,[2] and it is not
unreasonable to assume that the considerations which led him to
introduce 'filtering' into his account were similar to those which
must have been in Plato's mind when he introduced 'filtering'
into his account of the formation of gold. A man of Theophrastus'
temperament is not likely to have been attracted by Plato's far-
fetched application of the idea to the solidification of stones. But
in explaining the formation of gold Plato uses the idea in such
a way as to make it account for a familiar fact; and it is precisely
this use of the idea which would appeal to Theophrastus, who
attached so much importance to observation as a source of
knowledge.

If, then, Theophrastus thought that Plato's use of the idea of
'filtering' was appropriate in so far as it accounted for the formation of gold underground, one important conclusion may be
drawn, namely that in the *De Lapidibus* 'filtering' is likely to play
a part *in the formation of substances which occur in subterranean veins.*

We can also infer that for Theophrastus the vital distinction
between 'filtering' and 'a conflux' must lie in the *configuration* rather than in the quality of the substances to which they
respectively give rise. For there is no evidence that 'filtering'
produces a purer and more uniform matter than does 'a conflux',
although this is what at first sight a comparison of the two terms
might suggest. In § 2 Theophrastus implies that, so far as the
quality of the matter to be produced is concerned, it makes little
or no difference what process of separation is involved: it may be
'filtering' or 'a conflux' or some other process.[3] This is confirmed
by a remark in § 61, where Theophrastus turns to consider those
earths that are dug in earth-pits. These earths are formed of

---

[1] He offers no more than 'a probable account', this being all that the nature of
the subject would in his opinion permit. It is intended as 'a recreation', 'a sober
and sensible pastime' which gives an 'innocent pleasure' (*Timaeus* 59c–d).

[2] See *De Sensu et Sensibilibus*, §§ 83–91, *Metaphysica*, § 14, and frags. 28 and 29,
Wimmer.

[3] εἴτε συρροῆς εἴτε διηθήσεώς τινος γινομένης, εἴτε ὡς ἀνωτέρω εἴρηται καὶ κατ᾽
ἄλλον τρόπον ἐκκριμένης (sc. ὕλης). Here εἴτε suggests that the result is substantially
the same.

a 'conflux' (συρροή) or 'secretion' (ἔκκρισις)[1] purer and more uniform than are the others (namely those earths that are found with metals). Now these other earths are formed as the result either of 'a conflux' or of 'filtering' (§ 50). But if these earths, which *may* be formed by 'filtering', are necessarily less pure and less uniform than the earths of § 61, which *may* be formed by 'a conflux', it follows that the products of 'a conflux' *may* on occasion be purer and more uniform than those of 'filtering'.

The Conflux. If the true distinction between the products of 'filtering' and those of 'a conflux' lies in the configuration which they assume underground,[2] we have next to consider the geological structure exhibited by the products of 'a conflux'. The term συρροή, here translated 'conflux', in itself throws little light on the problem. Elsewhere Theophrastus speaks of 'a tear-like conflux' (δακρυώδης συρροή, *H.P.* 6. 6. 8) distilled by a plant, and of 'a sandy conflux of earth' (γῆς τις ἀμμώδης συρροή, *H.P.* 7. 15. 2), an accumulation of sandy earth on roof-tiles. The term σύρρευσις, however, which must be identical in meaning, is used in a more revealing manner by Aristotle, when he explains (*Historia Animalium* 551ᵇ27–29) that the larvae of gnats form in the slime of cisterns and wherever there is 'a conflux' (σύρρευσις) of water 'containing an earthy deposit' (γεώδη ἔχουσα ὑπόστασιν). This description provides an important clue. When 'a conflux' of water contains earthy matter in suspension, that matter forms a deposit as the water carrying it comes to rest. That a conflux was readily supposed to bring about a deposit is shown by Lucretius' use of the term 'confluere', which is obviously the Latin term corresponding to συρρεῖν: 'and all the slime of the world, so to speak, weighty as it was, flowed together to the lowest point and settled at the bottom like dregs.'[3]

---

[1] ἔκκρισις in this passage presumably covers all substances *not* produced by συρροή. That is, it includes the products (*a*) of διήθησις, (*b*) of the other processes of separation alluded to in § 2.

[2] *All* processes envisaged by Theophrastus must take place underground because he is discussing only 'things which are formed within the earth' (§ 1). See the Commentary ad loc.

[3] Book v. 496–7:

> ... atque omnis mundi quasi limus in imum
> confluxit grauis et subsedit funditus ut faex.

Although Lucretius speaks of slime, his use of dregs as an illustration shows that the process which he has in mind is one usually associated with matter suspended in a liquid.

A further clue is to be found in the *De Lapidibus* itself. After describing how various mineral substances may be produced artificially (§§ 56–59), Theophrastus remarks: 'from these examples it is clear that Art imitates Nature' (§ 60). The process described in the fullest detail is that used for producing artificial cinnabar (§ 58). Red sand found near Ephesus is ground and then washed. A sediment[1] is produced in the water, and the washing is repeated until the purified sediment is recognizable as cinnabar. An essential part of the process is the deposition of purified earthy matter suspended in water. But this, as we have seen, is precisely what appears to be the effect of a συρροή, and it is hard to resist the conclusion that the panning[2] of cinnabar described in § 58 is the artificial counterpart of a 'conflux' in nature.[3] That such a process might be conceived of as depositing not merely one layer of uniform matter, but several, is clear from Galen's detailed description of the preparation of Lemnian earth (xii, pp. 169–70, Kühn). According to this account, the priestess

---

[1] τὸ ὑφιστάμενον. Cf. the phrase γεώδης ὑπόστασις employed by Aristotle in the statement quoted above (*H.A.* 551ᵇ27–29).

[2] It may be noted that Callias, the inventor of the process, hoped that the sand would yield gold (§ 59). Now the process is almost identical with that used in panning gold-bearing material; so that a phrase quoted by Hesychius (s.v. προσφανῆ) from Theophrastus' lost work on metals, namely χρυσίου συρροάς (literally 'confluxes of gold'), may be taken to mean 'gold separated by panning'. In this phrase συρροή is used of the material produced by a conflux and not of the conflux itself. The same extension of the term is to be found in *De Lap.*, § 61, ἐκ συρροῆς τινος γίνεται . . . καθαρωτέρας καὶ ὁμαλωτέρας, where the expression 'purer and more uniform' must apply to the material, and not to the process by which it is produced.

[3] O. Regenbogen, 'Eine Forschungsmethode antiker Wissenschaft' (*Quellen und Studien zur Geschichte der Mathematik, Astronomie und Physik*, vol. i pt. ii (1931), pp. 131–82), discusses the use of analogy in Greek science and medicine. He shows that Theophrastus, like Aristotle, is far more cautious than earlier thinkers in the use of analogy as a method of demonstration. In the *De Causis Plantarum* he uses only analogies between plant and plant for the purpose of scientific proof. On the other hand, he refuses to draw positive conclusions from looser analogies, for example between plant and beast (Regenbogen, op. cit., pp. 155–6). The analogy which Theophrastus draws between natural and artificial production of minerals (*De Lap.*, § 60) is presumably a strict analogy which he would believe to provide a valid demonstration of the natural processes. He has already argued from a natural to an artificial process, in § 54. On the other hand, although Theophrastus may well have drawn an analogy between physiological and mineralogical processes in illustrating the formation of certain gemstones, it is doubtful whether he would have allowed himself to draw a definite conclusion from the argument, even though medical writers had previously used this analogy in reverse (see Regenbogen, op. cit., p. 137). For this reason, the attempt to discuss Theophrastus' views concerning the formation of gemstones in the light of this analogy (pp. 36–37) must necessarily be open to criticism.

mixes the natural earth with water and allows it to settle; she
then removes the surface water and finds two layers of earth, of
which the lower consists of stony and sandy matter, while the
upper layer is the rich medicinal earth.

A conflux, then, is the process whereby substances are formed
which occur not in veins, as with 'filtering', but in deposits.
The two kinds of geological structure which the processes produce in nature seem to be contrasted by Theophrastus himself
in § 51, where, discussing the earths found in mines, he writes:
'Cyanus is the least plentiful and is distributed in the smallest
quantities. Of the rest, some occur in veins (ῥάβδοι), while we are
told that ochre is found in masses (literally, 'is concentrated',
ἀθρόαν πως).' By 'concentrated', Theophrastus presumably means
'found in large, continuous deposits', and these are in fact the
conditions under which ochre is normally found. Since Theophrastus has already stated (§ 50) that these earths must be
generated either by 'a conflux' or by 'filtering',[1] it is tempting
to suppose that the concentrated deposits of ochre are to be
ascribed to the former process, and the veins of other earths to the
latter. 'Concentration' (ἀθροίζεσθαι) and 'conflux' (συρρεῖν) are
ideas that are likely to have been as closely linked in Theophrastus' mind as they were in Aristotle's.[2]

To go further and attempt to envisage each process as a geological phenomenon is merely to speculate. It is reasonable,
however, to suppose that, if water plays an essential part in the
'conflux', it must also be required in 'filtering'; indeed both processes require some form of motive power, and only water can
provide this adequately.[3] In 'filtering', then, water from the
earth's surface would carry down particles of earth and stone
through narrow fissures in the rock.[4] In this case, the coarser
material will presumably be trapped first, leaving the finer
material to travel further, or, as in the Samian earth-pit (§ 63), to

[1] ἤτοι συρροῆς τινος ἢ διηθήσεως γινομένης.
[2] See De Generatione Animalium 725ᵇ3-4, εἰς τούτους γὰρ ἀθροίζεται καὶ συρρεῖ.
[3] This water will also account conveniently for the presence of moisture as one of the ingredients of stones and earths. See pp. 18–20.
[4] Georgius Agricola (see p. 8), who was strongly influenced by Theophrastus' ideas, explains both processes in such terms (De Re Metallica, Libri xii, Basle, 1657, De Ortu et Causis Subterraneorum, iii, p. 508): 'aqua autem sic mista ramenta in unum aliquem canalis alveum rapit vel in angustias abducit quae ipsum (ipsa?) colando continent. utroque modo pura et aequalis materia ex quo gignitur terra subsidet.'

settle on top and then be covered by a fresh layer of coarse material.[1]

Where a 'conflux' is involved, the water will carry the earthy material down channels in the rocks into a subterranean cavity,[2] where the current of inflowing water will cause the material to settle into homogeneous layers, as in the processes described by Theophrastus and Galen (see pp. 24–25, above). To account for great deposits, such as the marble of Pentelicus (§ 6), enormous cavities would be needed, and the whole conception becomes almost fantastic.[3] But it might not have seemed fantastic to Theophrastus or to his students. That the earth was honeycombed with cavities was a natural supposition for men living among limestone mountains, and many Greek ideas were shaped by it.[4]

One crucial question is raised by this interpretation of the 'conflux' and of 'filtering'. If, as Theophrastus seems to imply in § 1, all stones, and not merely the more unusual kinds, are formed

[1] An illustration of such a process on a large scale may have been familiar to Theophrastus. Sir Charles Lyell, *Principles of Geology*, London, 1872, vol. ii, p. 527, describing the Katabothrai ('swallow-holes') of the Peloponnese, writes: 'As they are usually charged with fine sediment, and often with sand and pebbles, where they enter, whereas they are commonly pure and limpid where they flow out again, they must deposit much matter in empty spaces in the interior of the earth.'

[2] Thus, too, the percolation of rain-water appears to be prominent in Theophrastus' views on hydrology. See the article in *Phil. Suppl.* vii (1899), 280–1, 'Quellensucher im Altertum' by E. Oder, who quotes Seneca, *Nat. Quaest.* iii. 11. 5, 'causam siccitatis hanc ponit (sc. Theophrastus), quod obriguerit constricta tellus nec potuerit imbres inagitata transmittere.'

[3] Another fact to be explained would be the occurrence of such large deposits high up in a mountainous region, a problem which would be linked with the whole question of the formation of mountains. In Philo's *De Aeternitate Mundi*, chap. 25, there is a passage, which is usually thought to throw some light on Theophrastus' approach to this question. Here it is stated that 'the fiery matter enclosed within the earth' (τὸ κατακεκλεισμένον ἐν τῇ γῇ πυρῶδες) prevents the mountains from subsiding. This 'fiery matter' must be the dry exhalation, which also produces the 'fossiles', when it is enclosed underground (Aristotle, *Mete.* 378ᵃ15 ff.). This part of Philo's work, apart from insignificant additions, is usually held to reproduce Theophrastus' arguments against a Stoic rival. See E. Bignone, *L'Aristotele Perduto*, Florence, 1936, vol. ii, p. 456, n. 2. If Theophrastus argued that the upward pressure of the dry exhalation supported the mountains after they were formed, he may also have attributed their formation to the same cause.

[4] For instance, Greek ideas of the underworld. Again some thinkers were led by it to suppose that rivers were fed from underground lakes (Aristotle, *Mete.* 349ᵇ2 ff.), and Aristotle attributed earthquakes to subterranean winds (*Mete.* 365ᵇ21 ff.), an explanation frequently repeated by later writers. Incidentally, Plato's suggestion (*Timaeus* 60b–c; see pp. 20–21, above) that earth is hardened into stone by air-pressure presupposes an enclosed cavity.

within the earth, and if they are formed by processes requiring the passage of water through already existing stone, how were the first rocks formed? This at first sight is a formidable question, and yet it is not likely that Theophrastus ever put it to himself, since for him the answer would be obvious. Like Aristotle, he held that the earth was eternal, without beginning and without end (fr. 28, Wimmer). Consequently there was no need for him to provide in his theory for the necessary precondition of the processes which he adumbrated.

On the other hand, it is possible that Theophrastus did not mean to suggest that *all ordinary* stone is formed underground. In this case, since he knew of the existence of fossils in the quarries at Syracuse,[1] he might have deduced that rocks could be laid down by the sea, which would virtually be carrying out a gigantic 'conflux'. But we have no means of deciding the point. In any event, all the stones and earths which Theophrastus describes in the *De Lapidibus* are formed underground, and his theory was no doubt put forward with them alone in view.[2]

Other processes of 'separation' apart from the 'conflux' and

---

[1] Xenophanes ap. Hippolytum, *Philosophumena*, chap. xiv, H. Diels, *Fragmente der Vorsokratiker*, 7th edition, Xenophanes A 33; but the citation comes ultimately from the Φυσικῶν δόξαι of Theophrastus.

[2] The two processes, although distinct in character, would often be closely associated. For example, both play a part in the formation of springs. According to Aristotle (*Mete.* 350ª7 ff.), mountains catch the rainfall and cause the water to 'seep through (διαπιδῶσι) and flow together (συλλείβουσι) in minute quantities and in many places'. Here, διαπιδῶσι corresponds to διήθησις, and συλλείβουσι to συρροή. Again, both processes are at work in the kidneys (Arist. *De Partibus Animalium* 671ᵇ12 ff.). For (*a*) the blood-stream is *strained through* the body of the kidneys (διηθουμένων τῶν ὑγρῶν) leaving the blood itself to be concocted there, and (*b*) the residue *flows together* (συρρέῃ) into the middle of the kidneys, forming a deposit (ὑπόστασις) which passes into the bladder. Finally, it is possible that both διήθησις and συρροή had their counterpart in the preparation of ores, the former corresponding to the sifting of milled ore to secure uniformity (Strabo iii. 2. 9), and the latter to the concentration of the heavy metal, which would be separated from the rest of the sifted ore either by panning or by the use of inclined tables (Agatharchides, *De Mari Erythraeo* 27 and Diodorus Siculus iii. 14. 1–2). At both stages water would be used. For further details see C. E. N. Bromehead, 'Ancient Mining Processes', *Antiquity*, xvi (1942), 198–200. Inclined concentrating tables have been excavated at Laurium and may have been seen in action, along with mills and sieves, by Theophrastus.

It seems probable that in using διήθησις and συρροή to unlock the mysteries of mineralogy, Theophrastus was extending to a fresh sphere concepts which Aristotle had already applied to other problems of natural science. It is also possible that he was encouraged to do so because direct observation of certain artificial processes showed that these concepts were embodied in them.

'filtering' are referred to (§§ 2 and 61), but are not named. What these are we cannot tell. It is probable that stones occurring in unusual formations, such as the Lipara stone (§ 14), the pumices of Nisyros and Melos (§ 21), and the sard (§ 30) would be composed of matter 'separated in another way'.

The processes which have been discussed turn the raw material of stones and mineral earths into a 'pure, uniform matter', from which, according to Theophrastus, they derive some of their most important qualities, such as smoothness and solidity and, in the case of stones, lustre and transparency. These qualities vary according to the purity and uniformity of the constituent matter. Two qualities are conspicuous by their absence. These are colour (for lustre, τὸ στιλπνόν, implies no more than a shining surface) and hardness. Of these, colour must be considered later (see p. 38) but hardness leads us directly to the final stage of formation, the 'solidification' or 'hardening' of the pure, uniform matter through heat or cold.

C. *Solidification through Heat and Cold*

The translation of § 3 runs as follows : 'This solidification is due in some cases to heat and in others to cold, for there may be nothing to prevent certain kinds of stone from being formed either by heat or by cold; although it would seem that the earths at any rate are all formed by fire, since the process whereby a thing is solidified and the process whereby it suffers dissolution belong to contrary *genera*.'

The last statement must be discussed first since it reveals the principle which underlies the whole of this part of Theophrastus' theory. Solidification or hardening (πῆξις) and dissolution (τῆξις) belong to contrary *genera*. The meaning of this is made clear in Book iv of the *Meteorologica*, where it is explained that 'contrary causes have contrary effects'. Consequently, where solidification is due to heat, dissolution must be due to cold, and vice versa (*Mete.* 382ᵇ30 ff., 384ᵇ2 ff.).[1]

The application of this principle to the earths is, as Theophrastus appreciated, quite simple. They are dissolved, or rather disintegrated, by water, the characteristic qualities of which are the Moist and the Cold, and in particular the Cold (Aristotle, *De*

---

[1] For further details, see the Commentary ad loc.

Generatione et Corruptione 331 ᵃ3 ff.). Therefore they must be solidified by heat, that is, as Theophrastus himself states, by fire.[1] Furthermore, this is confirmed by observation: realgar and orpiment have, according to Theophrastus, obviously undergone combustion (§ 50). But this is true in fact of all the earths found in metal mines for 'all are products of the dry and smoky exhalation' (§ 50). Such a statement appears at first sight to involve an arbitrary extension of the hypothesis; yet this is not so in fact. For since the metals are composed of the moist exhalation and the two exhalations are normally found together,[2] both exhalations must exist in all metal mines. Thus for Theophrastus, as for Aristotle, it would be natural to suppose that all mineral earths found in mines were solidified by a conflagration caused by the dry exhalation.[3]

Whether Theophrastus believed that earths mined not in metal mines, but in separate earth-pits, such as those described in §§ 61–69, were solidified by heat from the dry exhalation is uncertain. There was not the same evidence to support the view. On the other hand, subterranean fire from some source must have solidified them, and it is difficult to imagine what this source in his opinion could have been, if it was not the dry exhalation.[4]

Theophrastus gives no clue as to the circumstances in which the pure, uniform matter composing the earths was solidified or hardened. He might conceivably have supposed that, when the cavities and fissures had been filled with the pure, uniform matter, the water which had carried it would be diverted elsewhere. The matter would then be left in a soft, moist state until it was eventually dried and hardened by the heat of the fire produced by the dry exhalation. Not all of the moisture, however, would be lost; for if this happened, the earths would lose their cohesion.[5]

---

[1] Cf. *Mete.* 383ᵃ1 ff.: τὰ μὲν γὰρ ὑπὸ ξηροῦ θερμοῦ (i.e. fire) παγέντα ὑπὸ ὕδατος λύεται, ὅ ἐστιν ὑγρὸν ψυχρόν.

[2] *Mete.* 358ᵃ21–22.

[3] The moist and dry exhalations are discussed more fully on pp. 38 ff. The dry exhalation is the source of the heat which hardens the mineral earths. It is obviously difficult to imagine how in the same locality metals were solidified by cold (see pp. 40–41) and mineral earths by heat. Possibly Theophrastus was not conscious of the difficulty. Aristotle (*De Generatione Animalium* 743ᵃ3 ff.) is quite content to suppose that heat and cold are simultaneously at work in forming the parts of the body, the former in solidifying the sinews and bones, and the latter the flesh.

[4] The same may be said of *stones* formed by heat and underground.

[5] See *De Igne*, § 8, quoted on p. 19, n. 1.

Apart from hardness, another property which may be imparted to an earth by burning is innate heat, where it exists, as for example in gypsum. The presence of this innate heat is proof for Theophrastus that gypsum 'is generated by fire' (§ 69), but why only certain of the substances thus generated should possess it is not explained.

Finally heat seems to bring about modifications in the colour of earths. Theophrastus asserts (§ 54), that the artificial method of producing ruddle from ochre by roasting in pots is 'similar to, or comparable with, the natural process of generation' and that 'fire would appear to be the agent responsible for all these transformations'.[1]

Earths, then, are solidified by heat, and may be affected by it in other ways. The solidification of stones was for Theophrastus a more complex problem, for here no simple criterion was available. The process whereby stones are solidified cannot be readily deduced from any process of dissolution. On the one hand, stones do not disintegrate in water, as earth does.[2] As for fusion by fire, Theophrastus knew of certain people, probably smelters and lime-burners, who claimed that fire would melt all stones except limestone (μάρμαροι), which when burnt was reduced to powder (§ 9). If Theophrastus had accepted this assertion, he could have drawn the conclusion that all stones, with the exception of limestone, are solidified by cold. However, he rejects the statement as an exaggeration on the ground that many stones, when exposed to fire, behave with the same recalcitrance as earthenware (§ 10). He mentions only three kinds of stones that are melted by fire; and in all three cases he introduces factors which would have prevented him from concluding definitely that they had been solidified by cold. These stones are slag, 'pyromachi', and millstones, all of which receive attention in § 9.

Slag. Theophrastus states that when silver, copper, and iron are melted their slag ('the stone from them') melts with them. He suggests two explanations: the slag melts either (*a*) because of the moist character of its constituents, or (*b*) owing to the presence of the metals, which are themselves moist ('of water', § 1; see p. 16).

---

[1] See further on p. 38.

[2] Substances that are solidified by heat are dissolved by water, unless, like earthenware, they have contracted so much that water cannot enter their pores (*Mete.* 385^{a}22 ff.). Stone, like earthenware, is insoluble (*Mete.* 384^{a}33 ff.).

If the former explanation were true, Theophrastus could have deduced that slag is solidified by cold. The description given in *Meteorologica* iv (383ª26 ff.) would be applicable: 'among those substances *solidified by cold* which contain more earth than water although they are common to both, those which are solidified when heat departs from them are melted by heat when it enters into them again.'

If, however, the second explanation is true, then the melting has nothing to do with the character of the slag itself; it is caused merely by the association of the slag with something else, a metal. In this case, we know nothing about the nature and behaviour of slag as such, and can therefore learn nothing about the way in which it was solidified.

Thus slag is presumably one of those stones which Theophrastus has in mind when he writes that 'there may be nothing to prevent certain kinds of stone from being formed by either of these two things' (§ 3), that is, either by heat or by cold. If the first explanation is true, slag is solidified by cold; if the second is true, it might, for all that we know, have been solidified by heat, but we cannot know for certain.

'*Pyromachi*' *and millstones.* A passage in Book iv of the *Meteorologica* (383ᵇ5 ff.) refers to both types of stones: 'the stone "pyrimachus"[1] melts in such a way as to drip and become fluid: after being fluid, it solidifies and becomes hard again. Millstones also melt so as to become fluid.' This passage follows closely upon one that has been quoted above in connexion with slag. In this previous passage (*Mete.* 383ª26 ff.), we have a description of substances which contain more earth than water, and which are solidified by cold but melted by heat. The 'pyrimachus' and millstones are cited as instances of such substances. Thus the author implies that both kinds of stone have been solidified by cold, and clearly regards the fact that they are melted by heat as proof of this.

Theophrastus, however, adds an important qualification when he states that ' "pyromachi" and millstones become fluid *along with the material placed upon them*' (§ 9), the material in question being in all probability a flux.[2] He thus raises the same doubts

---

[1] In the *Meteorologica* the stones are called πυριμάχος and μύλαι, while in the *De Lapidibus* they are termed πυρομάχοι and μυλίαι respectively. There can be little doubt that both passages refer to the same two kinds of stone.

[2] See the Commentary.

22

2

2

as to their formation and solidification as he has just previously raised in regard to slag. If 'pyromachi' and millstones melted because of their own moisture, one could deduce that they had been solidified by cold. If, on the other hand, they melted only because the presence of other materials caused them to do so, no conclusions as to their solidification could be drawn. In hinting at this important distinction Theophrastus no doubt wished to criticize the over-facile interpretation of Aristotle, if indeed it was he who was the author of *Meteorologica* iv. Like slag, 'pyromachi' and millstones must have ranked for Theophrastus as instances of stones that might prove to have been solidified either by heat or by cold.[1]

Theophrastus mentions three kinds of stones that are melted by fire,[2] and could not conclude outright that any of them was solidified by cold. Thus, when he considered the formation of stones in general, he could find no evidence that solidification by cold was in any one case more than a bare possibility. This fact explains the form of the statement made by him in § 3: 'This solidification is due in some cases to heat and in others to cold, for there may be nothing to prevent certain kinds of stone from being formed by either of these things.' The cautious wording of the final remark reflects Theophrastus' doubts (see the Commentary ad loc.) : he is not certain whether any stones are in fact formed by cold, and his statements concerning slag, 'pyromachi', and millstones show why this is so.

Could Theophrastus, then, have reasonably inferred that all stones that are *not* melted by heat are solidified by heat? Unfortunately, this was not possible for him if he accepted a certain proposition which is advanced in *Meteorologica* iv. Of course, all such stones *might* have been solidified by heat, and this would indeed explain why they are not melted by heat. But according to the author of *Meteorologica* iv, solidification by cold also might account for this. Cold, as we have seen above, solidifies substances composed of both earth and water by expelling the heat. Heat will cause such a substance to melt when it enters the substance again;

---

[1] Slag may conceivably be among the 'many nameless stones' that are said to be melted by heat (*Mete.* 389ᵃ8–9). If so, here again Theophrastus was correcting his predecessor.

[2] If it is asked why he did not mention more varieties of such stones, the answer would be that not many types of stone could have been melted at the comparatively low temperatures attained by ancient methods of firing.

and this is what happens to the 'pyrimachus' and to millstones, as they are presented to us in *Meteorologica* iv. But if the heat, as it departs, completely[1] evaporates the moisture in the substance, then melting cannot take place when heat is again present (*Mete.* 383ᵃ29 ff.; 388ᵇ13 ff.). Such an intense process of solidification by cold is distinguished in *Meteorologica* iv as 'chilling', 'refrigeration' (ψῦξις).[2] Amber and 'certain stones', such as stalactites in caves, are cited as examples; and these cannot be melted (*Mete.* 388ᵇ24 ff.).

Theophrastus does not use the term ψῦξις, nor was he bound to do so since it denotes a difference of degree rather than of kind, and might well have been subsumed by him under the heading of 'the cold' (τὸ ψυχρόν). In any case, he could hardly have supposed that 'refrigeration' played more than a limited part in the solidification of stones. Of the substances discussed by Theophrastus only one, amber, is stated in *Meteorologica* iv to be formed by refrigeration; and the fact cited in support of this assertion, namely that 'it is cooled by the river' (*Mete.* 388ᵇ21), is not one that he would have been likely to accept as true. He seems to dissociate himself from this version of its origin, and supposes the amber of Liguria to be dug from the earth (§ 29). If he had felt justified in risking such speculations, the concept of 'refrigeration' might have helped him to explain the formation of products of the sea, pearls (§ 35) and coral (§ 38), or what he imagined to be such, namely pumice formed from sea-foam (§§ 19, 22; cf. [Aristotle] *de Plantis* 823ᵇ). But there is no evidence that he attempted anything of the kind.

The comments made by Theophrastus concerning slag, 'pyromachi', and millstones lead to the conclusion that there were no stones which he could confidently suppose to be solidified by cold. On the other hand, it seems reasonably certain that, had he so wished, he could have established to his own satisfaction that several groups of stones are solidified by heat. These are (1) limestone (μάρμαροι), (2) some kinds of pumice, (3) certain precious stones, and (4) certain combustible stones.

---

[1] 'Completely' needs qualification. Enough moisture must be left to hold the ingredients together, as Alexander of Aphrodisias mentions in his comment. See also pp. 18–20.

[2] 'Refrigeration' is the rendering of E. W. Webster, *Meteorologica* in *The Works of Aristotle translated into English*, vol. iii, Oxford, 1931. H. D. P. Lee (*Meteorologica*, Loeb Classical Library, Harvard, 1952) translates the word by 'cold', 'cooling', and so fails to make the distinction clear.

1. *Limestone.* The evidence comes from two passages. In § 9 he quotes, without disputing it, the fact that when μάρμαροι are burnt, they are transformed into lime (κονία). The subject of the second passage, *De Igne*, § 46, is a stone used for making sarcophagi.[1] This stone 'consumes everything and turns its contents into ashes. For in it also the heat is exceptional. That the stone produces its effect by heat and because it is hot by nature is shown by the fact that lime (κονία) comes from it.' This stone is linked with the μάρμαροι by its transformation into lime. It is also linked with the gypsum of *De Lap.*, § 69, in respect of its innate heat, and the gypsum moreover is said to have some of the properties of lime (τὰ τῆς κονίας, § 68). In view of its nature, Theophrastus is prepared to believe that gypsum is 'generated by fire' (§ 69), and he is likely to have held the same view of the μάρμαροι and the sarcophagus stone, which share certain of their characteristics with it.

2. *Pumice.* Here Theophrastus is more explicit. After explaining that pumice is non-inflammable and fireproof because it contains no moisture, he writes that 'pumice in general is held by some to be produced through a process of combustion (ἐκ κατακαύσεως), except for the kind that is formed of sea-foam' (§ 19). Theophrastus is too cautious to accept such an assertion outright. In fact, he suggests that there may be several modes of generation (§ 21). At the same time he brings forward evidence for the view, particularly the occurrence of pumice in volcanic regions (§ 20), and clearly regards this as cogent. He could hardly deny that the pumice of Sicily (§ 22) and of Lipara (§ 14) was formed by heat, even if he refused to draw conclusions as to the other kinds.

3. *Precious stones associated with metals.* The mineral earths found in metal mines are certainly solidified by fire from the dry exhalation (§ 50); and it would be natural for Theophrastus to suppose that any associated stones which he thought to be non-fusible were also formed by fire. At the same time it would not be easy for him to draw any positive conclusion since the necessary evidence was lacking. In the case of the earths, he had observed

[1] The reading of the MSS. ὁ δ' ἐν κύκλῳ λίθος is corrupt. H. Blumner, *Technologie und Terminologie der Gewerbe und Künste bei Griechen und Römern*, Leipzig, 1875–87, vol. iii, p. 60, n. 2, mentions ἐν Ἄσσῳ as an emendation for ἐν κύκλῳ. A more plausible reading is ὁ δ' ἐν Λυκίᾳ λίθος. Stones of this kind both from Assos and from Lycia are referred to by Pliny (xxxvi. 131).

that some showed clear signs of combustion (§ 50) ; and there was in any case a presumption that earths were formed by fire (§ 3) because they disintegrated in water. Nevertheless, Theophrastus might feel reasonably certain that some stones of this class were formed by fire. For example, he could hardly doubt that the 'cyanus' (§§ 31, 37) was solidified by fire, like the earth of the same name (§§ 40, 51, 55), for he recognized their kinship.[1] Again, he might be tempted to conclude, on more slender evidence, that since the 'smaragdi' of Demonesus and Cyprus were found in copper-mines (§ 25), they too were formed by fire.

4. *Certain combustible stones.* Theophrastus might have been predisposed by certain pieces of evidence to think that some at least of the stones discussed in §§ 12–17 were formed by heat. For instance, the 'stone' (probably palygorskite; see the Commentary) which had been found in the mines of Scaptehyle (§ 17), where gold and silver were to be found (Lucretius vi. 810), was presumably solidified by heat from the dry exhalation, like the earths which are associated with metals. The same might be true of the stone of Cape Erineas (§ 15), but for a different reason. This emits bituminous fumes (§ 15) and is in fact asphalt. Now asphalt is found in 'burning places', as members of the Peripatetic School knew ([Aristotle] *De Mir. Aus.* 842^{b}15 ff., chap. 127) ; and its association with the subterranean fire could have led Theophrastus to ascribe its generation to fire from the dry exhalation. He might well have ascribed a similar origin to the lignite of Binae (§§ 12–13) since he links it with the asphalt of Cape Erineas (§ 15). Finally, the combustible Lipara stone (§ 14; probably pitchstone) must surely in his view have been formed by heat since the region was volcanic.

Thus there was a moderate number of stones to which Theophrastus could reasonably have assigned heat as the agent of their formation.[2] Again, as we have seen, he would not have

[1] This seems clear from § 39, where he speaks of a *natural* (αὐτοφυής) cyanus-stone which contains chrysocolla. 'Natural' has no sense unless we are to connect the cyanus-stone with the *natural* cyanus-*earth*, which in § 55 is distinguished from the artificial kind.

[2] Why heat should cause the pure, uniform matter to produce sometimes earths and sometimes stones is nowhere explained. The reference in § 50 to earths that are 'apt to harden to the consistency of stone' (πρὸς τὴν ἀπολίθωσιν εὐφυεῖς) suggests that the properties of the pure, uniform matter may have been the determining factor. It is impossible to say whether a longer exposure to the heat also played

excluded the possibility that cold is the formative agent of a few more. But many would necessarily be left unaccounted for, and his cautious approach to the problem in his introduction was fully justified by the difficulties confronting him.

The formation of gemstones. In § 27 Theophrastus writes: 'It is stated that in Cyprus a stone was once found, one half of which was a "smaragdus" and the other half an "iaspis", as though the transformation of the stone from water were not yet complete.' The implications of this passage are far from clear, but one point at least is certain: Theophrastus cannot have meant to imply that some gemstones are made up of water,[1] since this would contradict his first proposition that stones, precious stones included, are of earth (§ 1). Moreover, the special characteristics of gemstones, transparency (τὸ διαφανές) and lustre (τὸ στιλπνόν), are stated in § 2 to be due to the purity and uniformity of the constituent matter. They cannot then be due to a fundamental difference in the ingredients involved.[2]

A tentative explanation of the passage in § 27 may be offered in the light of Theophrastus' fantastic description of 'lyngurium' (§ 28). This stone, as its name implies, was commonly supposed to be formed from the excreted urine of the lynx. Theophrastus, so far from discrediting this notion in accordance with his usual sceptical caution, actually elaborates it with details possibly contributed by the physician Diocles (see the Commentary ad loc.), who made a study of the urinary tract. Theophrastus tells us that the stone of a wild lynx is 'better' than that of a tame lynx, and the stone of a male 'better' than that of a female. The difference is due to diet, habits, and physique. What is meant by 'better' is not stated, but it does not mean 'more transparent' because the male stone is less transparent than the female (§ 31). Most likely

a part. Theophrastus may have believed this to be so, since he had observed that some stones at least become excessively hard through prolonged exposure to the sun (§ 11).

[1] There is no reason to suspect the text.

[2] Here he probably differed from Aristotle, who, if Stobaeus (*Ecl.* 1. 52) may be trusted, maintained that 'not only was air transparent, but also water and certain things composed of it, such as glass, crystal, and certain bright stones'. It is significant that in the *Meteorologica* (389ᵃ8–9) glass and many nameless stones are said to be of water because they are melted by heat. Theophrastus makes no mention of any such class of stone, while as for glass, he had received hints of its true origin (§ 49). Consequently, he was aware that transparency might belong to earthy matter, as well as to water, and this would mean that transparency in stones must be accounted for in a different way.

it refers to the darker colour of the male stone (loc. cit.). It seems evident, however, that according to Theophrastus there are differences in the urine which are imparted to the stones.

The actual formation of the stones was perhaps believed by him to be accomplished by a process similar to that which was thought to take place when stone is formed in human organs.[1] This process is explained in a passage from a Peripatetic source, which may be derived from Theophrastus:[2] 'Man has a bladder, and also a stem which is narrow for its size. Because he has this organ, earthy matter is compressed into the bladder (hence chamberpots are stained by it), and because of the warmth of the region, the matter is concocted and thickened; it remains there and is augmented because of the narrow ureter. For since the earthy deposits cannot easily pass out, they turn back on each other and form stone.' In some important respects the process here described reminds us of those discussed earlier. Both 'filtering' and solidification by heat play a part, and it is not unreasonable to suppose that Theophrastus might well have believed a number of precious stones to be formed by a process analogous to this.

We may now return to § 27. It is clear from Theophrastus' comments on the 'lyngurium' that in the formation of a transparent stone there may be a somewhat unusual relationship between the earthy matter and the water which carries it. In particular we must suppose that the proportion of water to earthy matter is immeasurably greater than in the case of the other stones and the mineral earths; moreover, the earthy particles are so small as virtually to lose their identity in the fluid. The water is more than merely a vehicle for the matter which is deposited; it is actually impregnated with it. Thus Theophrastus may be writing loosely, but from his own point of view not altogether without justification when he states that the 'transformation *from water* was not yet complete'.

The part of the stone that was 'smaragdus' was presumably a bright green stone, and the rest of it a stone of a duller colour. Theophrastus may have thought that the dull colour was the

[1] He would, however, be extremely cautious in using such an analogy. See p. 24, n. 3.
[2] *Problems*, x. 43, 895ª36 ff. H. Diels, 'Aristotelica', *Hermes*, xl (1905), 215–16, argues that most of the collection of *Problems* is taken from the minor works of Theophrastus.

original colour derived from the fluid, and that the green was a modification introduced by further heating, just as yellow ochre is turned into red ochre by baking (§ 54).

Colour. This last point suggests an answer to a question which was raised at an earlier stage of the discussion (p. 28). In the introduction to the *De Lapidibus* the colour of stones and mineral earths is not mentioned either as a property of the pure, uniform matter or as a result of the process of solidification. At what stage, then, is colour produced? The answer presumably is: at either stage or at both. But we may probably qualify this statement by adding that only solidification by *heat* will produce a change of colour in the final stage of formation. For the transformation of yellow ochre into red ochre meets with the comment (§ 54) that 'fire would appear to be the agent responsible for all these transformations'.

Appendix: Aristotle's Theory of the Formation of Metals and Minerals[1]

The twofold exhalation. Aristotle explains in Book i of the *Meteorologica* (341ᵇ6 ff.) that the heat of the sun causes the earth to give off an exhalation (ἀναθυμίασις), which is of two kinds. One kind, derived from the moisture within the earth and on its surface, is a moist vapour (cf. *De Sensu* 443ᵃ26–27), 'potentially like water' (340ᵇ28–29); the other, which comes from the earth itself, is hot, dry, and smoky, highly combustible 'like a fuel' (οἷον ὑπέκκαυμα, 341ᵇ18–19), 'the most inflammable of substances' (341ᵇ16–17), 'potentially like fire' (340ᵇ29), and compounded of Air and Earth (*De Sensu* 443ᵃ21–22, 27–28).

The moist exhalation, then, is a vapour. The dry exhalation, on the other hand, is less easy to envisage, as Aristotle himself admits (341ᵇ15), but in some of its states it is fiery and in others not unlike a gas.

Books i–iii of the *Meteorologica* are largely devoted to a consideration of the phenomena caused by the two exhalations.[2] For instance, rain, dew, frost, and snow are attributed to the moist, vaporous kind; shooting stars, thunder, lightning, wind, and earthquakes to the dry, smoky kind. At the end of Book iii

---

[1] Reprinted from *Classical Quarterly*, xliii (1949), 141–6.

[2] Aristotle speaks sometimes of a twofold exhalation, sometimes of two exhalations.

(378ᵃ15 ff.) comes the passage which is the subject of this paper. Here Aristotle describes what happens when the two exhalations are 'imprisoned within parts of the earth'. Two substances are formed in the earth, 'fossiles'[1] (τὰ ὀρυκτά) and metals (τὰ μεταλλευόμενα), and of these the metals are produced from the vaporous exhalation and the 'fossiles' by the dry one. The formation of the metals is clear in principle, but obscure in detail. On the other hand, the part played by the dry exhalation in producing the 'fossiles' is obscure in every respect and will be considered later, although it is treated first by Aristotle himself.

The formation of the metals, 378ᵃ26 ff.: τῆς δ' ἀναθυμιάσεως τῆς ἀτμιδώδους, ὅσα μεταλλεύεται, καὶ ἔστιν ἢ χυτὰ ἢ ἐλατά, οἷον σίδηρος, χρυσός, χαλκός. ποιεῖ δὲ ταῦτα πάντα ἡ ἀναθυμίασις ἡ ἀτμιδώδης ἐγκατακλειομένη, καὶ μάλιστα ἐν τοῖς λίθοις, διὰ ξηρότητα εἰς ἓν συνθλιβομένη καὶ πηγνυμένη, οἷον ἢ δρόσος ἢ πάχνη, ὅταν ἀποκριθῇ. ἐνταῦθα δὲ πρὶν ἀποκριθῆναι γεννᾶται ταῦτα. διὸ ἔστι μὲν ὡς ὕδωρ ταῦτα, ἔστιν δ' ὡς οὔ· δυνάμει μὲν γὰρ ἡ ὕλη ὕδατος ἦν, ἔστι δ' οὐκέτι, οὐδ' ἐξ ὕδατος γενομένου διά τι πάθος, ὥσπερ οἱ χυμοί· οὐδὲ γὰρ οὕτω γίγνεται τὸ μὲν χαλκὸς τὸ δὲ χρυσός, ἀλλὰ πρὶν γενέσθαι παγείσης τῆς ἀναθυμιάσεως ἕκαστα τούτων ἐστίν. διὸ καὶ πυροῦται πάντα καὶ γῆν ἔχει· ξηρὰν γὰρ ἔχει ἀναθυμίασιν· ὁ δὲ χρυσὸς μόνος οὐ πυροῦται.[2]

(*a*) τῆς δ' ἀναθυμιάσεως . . . ἐν τοῖς λίθοις. By metals Aristotle means all those substances which are mined and which, unlike the 'fossiles', are fusible or malleable (ἢ χυτὰ ἢ ἐλατά). As instances he mentions iron, gold, and copper, but a fuller list would have included silver, tin (388ᵃ13), and probably lead (389ᵃ7).[3] These are all formed by the moist exhalation[4] when it is trapped underground, and particularly if it is trapped in rocks (καὶ μάλιστα ἐν τοῖς λίθοις). This, no doubt, is meant partly to explain why

[1] This is E. W. Webster's rendering of the term in the Oxford translation and is convenient, however archaic. The distinction between 'things dug' (τὰ ὀρυκτά) and 'things mined' (τὰ μεταλλευόμενα) seems at first sight arbitrary. Aristotle merely uses the two terms as labels for distinguishing two groups of natural substances. They do not imply a subtle difference between digging and mining as such.

[2] The text is that of F. H. Fobes, Cambridge, Mass., 1919.

[3] Book iv of the *Meteorologica* expounds the formation and properties of homogeneous substances in general and contains several references to metals and stones which are of value. Where there is no further indication, the references in this paper are to the *Meteorologica*.

[4] It has often been pointed out that this theory of a common origin of all metals encouraged the alchemists in their efforts to transmute base metals into gold. There is no reason to suppose that such a possibility ever occurred to Aristotle.

metals have to be extracted from ores. Similarly, according to Plato, *Tim.* 59b, metals are formed by the percolation of 'fusible water' (χυτὰ ὕδατα) through rock.

(*b*) διὰ ξηρότητα . . . γεννᾶται ταῦτα. The exhalation is compressed (εἰς ἓν συνθλιβομένη, that is, condensed) by the dryness of the rocks and congealed or solidified (πηγνυμένη), 'just like dew or hoar-frost, when it has been separated. But in this case, the metals are formed before it has been separated.'

This is a difficult passage. The moist exhalation condenses when it comes into contact with the dry rock, and is there congealed into metals, presumably by cold. (The point will be discussed below.) Aristotle then writes 'like dew or hoar-frost'. But this is misleading because hoar-frost does not condense (347ª13 ff.) and dew does not congeal. What he might have said was 'condensed like dew and congealed like hoar-frost'. However, the real object of the comparison is to mark a contrast. Unlike either dew or hoar-frost, the metals are formed before it (i.e. the moist exhalation) has been separated from the dry exhalation. This is Alexander's explanation[1] and is no doubt correct because the metals 'contain the dry exhalation' (378ᵇ3–4). There is nothing strange in this conception since normally the two exhalations are closely associated, or rather 'mixed'.[2]

'Compressed by the dryness of the rocks and congealed'. Does Aristotle mean that the dryness of the rocks not only condenses but also congeals and solidifies the moist exhalation? Probably not. In fact, he has already implied as much by stating that the metals are 'fusible or malleable' (378ª27). By 'fusible', of course, he means 'melted by heat'. 'Gold, silver, copper, tin, lead . . . are of water;[3] for all of them are melted by heat' (389ª7 ff.). Now Aristotle accepted as axiomatic the principle that 'melting', 'dissolution' (τῆξις), and 'hardening', 'congealing', 'solidification' (πῆξις) must be due in every case to opposite causes; furthermore, he supposed both to be caused either by dry heat or by cold (382ᵇ31 ff.). Consequently if gold, silver, &c., are melted by heat, they must have been hardened by cold. The same is true of iron, which is malleable rather than fusible, that

---

[1] *Comm. in Meteor.*, ed. Hayduck, p. 177. 27–33.
[2] 358ª21–22, μεμιγμένης δ' οὔσης, ὥσπερ εἴπομεν, τῆς τε ἀτμιδώδους ἀναθυμιάσεως καὶ τῆς ξηρᾶς.
[3] Because the moist exhalation is potentially a kind of water.

is, it is normally softened by heat and melted only by excessive heat (383ᵃ29 ff.); iron, too, must have been hardened by cold.

(c) διὸ ἔστι μὲν ὡς ὕδωρ ταῦτα . . . ἕκαστα τούτων ἐστίν. Because the moist exhalation composing the metals contains an admixture of the dry exhalation, the metals cannot revert to water (as, for instance, hoar-frost can). 'Their matter was potentially that of water, but is so no longer. Nor, like savours, do the metals come from water which has been transformed into them by being affected in some way (οὐδ' ἐξ ὕδατος γενομένου διά τι πάθος, ὥσπερ οἱ χυμοί). Copper and gold were not formed in this way either. No; each of the metals exists because the exhalation congealed before water could be formed' (378ᵃ33–378ᵇ3).

The formation of the metals differs from that of dew and hoar-frost. It also differs from that of savours. According to Aristotle (De Sensu 441ᵇ17 ff.), natural savours are produced when water filters through earthy matter and thus acquires a new quality. This is the πάθος which water must undergo in order to be transformed into a savour. Aristotle warns us not to think of the generation of the metals in this way. He does not want us to suppose that the moist exhalation is first condensed into water, which is then transformed into metals by the addition of some other ingredient. On the contrary, the ingredients, the moist exhalation plus an admixture of the dry exhalation, are there from the start, and are condensed and hardened together. Just as the metals can no longer revert to actual water, so, too, they never came from actual water 'because the exhalation congealed before water could be formed'.

(d) διὸ καὶ πυροῦται . . . οὐ πυροῦται. 'Hence all the metals are affected by fire and contain earth, for they all contain the dry exhalation. Only gold is unaffected by fire.' Since the metals contain earthy matter, exposure to fire causes them to produce dross, as Alexander points out (op. cit., p. 178. 6–10), and incidentally to change colour. Olympiodorus adds that for the same reason they rust (ἰοῦσθαι).[1] No doubt Aristotle had all these facts in mind. The exception is gold; presumably pure gold is meant, as Alexander observes.

Possibly the presence of earthy matter in different proportions may have served to explain the difference between the baser and the more precious metals. Theoretically, they could all have been

---

[1] Comm. in Meteor., ed. Stüve, p. 270. 24–25.

arranged in a series, with gold, containing the smallest quantity
of the dry exhalation, at one end of the scale, and iron, containing
the greatest, at the other. (Iron contains a large proportion of
earthy matter and for this reason can be softened, but not easily
melted: 383ᵃ29 ff.)

The moist exhalation, then, is the material of the metals. Along
with portions of the dry exhalation it is trapped underground,
where it condenses, particularly if it comes into contact with rocks,
and then hardens, probably through cold. Metals are not formed
like dew or hoar-frost, still less like savours. Because the metals
contain earthy matter, they cannot revert to water, and for the
same reason they are, with the exception of pure gold, affected
by fire.

The formation of the 'fossiles'. It has always been readily assumed that the function of the dry exhalation in forming the
'fossiles' is like that of the moist exhalation in forming the metals.
The moist exhalation is predominantly the *matter* of which the
metals are formed. What could be more natural than to suppose
that the dry exhalation is similarly the *matter* of which the
'fossiles' are composed?

And yet this view can hardly be the correct one, although it
rests on excellent authority[1] and has the advantage of symmetry.
In fact, its symmetry has probably been responsible for its wide
acceptance; or, to be more exact, its symmetry coupled with the
obscurities in Aristotle's all too brief statement (378ᵃ21–26): ἡ
μὲν οὖν ξηρὰ ἀναθυμίασίς ἐστιν ἥ τις ἐκπυροῦσα ποιεῖ τὰ ὀρυκτὰ
πάντα, οἷον λίθων τε γένη τὰ ἄτηκτα καὶ σανδαράκην καὶ ὤχραν καὶ
μίλτον καὶ θεῖον καὶ τἆλλα τὰ τοιαῦτα. τὰ δὲ πλεῖστα τῶν ὀρυκτῶν

---

[1] Thus Alexander (op. cit., p. 177. 15–18) writes τὰ μὲν γὰρ αὐτῶν ὀρυκτὰ εἶναι, ἃ
ποιεῖν τὴν ξηράν τε καὶ καπνώδη ἀναθυμίασιν σ υ ν ι σ τ α μ έ ν η ν, ὅταν πλεονάσῃ. Olympiodorus is in substantial agreement (see below). The view was adopted, with modifications, by the Arabs (see E. J. Holmyard and D. C. Mandeville, *Avicennae de
Congelatione et Conglutinatione Lapidum*, p. 35, footnote), and is restated by Iacobus
Zabarella (*De Rebus Naturalibus*, Cologne, 1594, *De Naturalis Scientiae Constitutione*,
chap. 30, p. 85b). Both Zeller (*Aristotle and the Earlier Peripatetics*, i, p. 515) and Ross
(*Aristotle*, p. 111) appear to accept the tradition. Thus Ross: '. . . These are divided
into the metals, which are formed by the moist exhalation, and the "fossiles",
formed by the dry.' 'By' is ambiguous, but the two processes are obviously
supposed to be analogous. W. Capelle, who refers to the topic in his article
'Meteorologie' (*P.W. Suppl.* vi, col. 341), unfortunately does not discuss it. J. L.
Ideler in his edition of the *Meteorologica* allows Alexander and Olympiodorus
to speak for Aristotle. Translators have sometimes come nearer to the truth
than the commentators.

ἐστιν τὰ μὲν κονία κεχρωματισμένη, τὰ δὲ λίθος ἐκ τοιαύτης γεγονὼς συστάσεως, οἷον τὸ κιννάβαρι.[1] 'It is the dry exhalation, then, that forms all the "fossiles" by burning them (?), as for example those kinds of stones which cannot be melted and realgar, ochre, ruddle, sulphur, and other things of that kind. Most of the "fossiles" are either coloured powder-ash (?) or, like cinnabar, a stone formed of a similar composition.'

There is much in this admittedly difficult passage which points to one conclusion alone, that the dry exhalation is not the material cause of the 'fossiles', as commentators have usually supposed, but their efficient cause, supplying the heat which forms them.

(a) To take a comparatively simple detail first: the 'fossiles' include not only certain minerals such as realgar, ochre, ruddle, sulphur, and cinnabar, but also those kinds of stones which cannot be melted.

Now if the dry exhalation is to be regarded as the material of the 'fossiles', an immense disproportion in bulk must exist between its products and those of the moist exhalation, when either is trapped underground. The minerals such as ochre, ruddle, &c., might by themselves be supposed to be roughly equivalent in bulk to the metals. But what of the stones which cannot be melted? Aristotle nowhere gives a list of such stones, but it seems likely that he must have included under them at least the crystalline limestones, for it was a familiar and undeniable fact that such stones, when burnt, did not melt, but turned into lime.[2] Hence some of the most important mountain masses known to Aristotle must have been classed among stones that cannot be melted. To provide material for these, the dry exhalation must have accumulated underground in such quantities as would altogether have upset the balance which was clearly assumed to exist between it and the moist exhalation. (See, for example, 360^{b}15 ff.)

(b) An even plainer hint as to the truth lies in the word ἐκπυροῦσα. The dry exhalation forms the 'fossiles' by burning them. It is not clear what is to be understood as the object of ἐκπυροῦσα, but it is probably the 'fossiles' themselves, or, rather, the material of which they are formed.[3] One thing at least is

---

[1] The text, as before, is that of F. H. Fobes.

[2] Theophrastus, De Lapidibus, § 9.

[3] Thus Barthélemy Saint-Hilaire translates ἡ μὲν οὖν ξηρὰ ἀναθυμίασις κτλ. 'L'exhalaison sèche, en brûlant les matières, produit tous les minéraux, etc.' Similarly E. W. Webster (Oxford translation) has 'the heat of the dry exhalation

certain: ἐκπυροῦσα must be active in meaning. It cannot be intransitive ('catching fire'), as Olympiodorus seems to think,[1] for in the writings of Aristotle and Theophrastus at least there is no trace of such a use.[2] Thus the dry exhalation supplies not the matter, but the heat which forms the 'fossiles'. We have already seen (p. 38) that it is highly inflammable. When set in motion, it easily ignites and so produces shooting stars, thunder, and lightning (341^b ff., 369^a ff.). Within the earth it will similarly ignite if it is set in motion (367^{a}9 ff., with Webster's note), and this is 'the cause of the fire that is generated within the earth', for 'there exists within the earth much heat and fire' (360^{a}5–6). When the exhalation is in this fiery state, it must tend to rise to the earth's surface. But if in so doing it is trapped underground and brought into contact with the right materials, it will by combustion transform these materials into 'fossiles'.

(c) The text still provides one serious obscurity. Most of the 'fossiles' are κονία κεχρωματισμένη. What is this? In Attic prose κονία, which has the same root as κόνις, dust, means

(1) Fine powdery ash (such as was used as a detergent). In this sense it is often associated with τέφρα, which also means 'ash', 'cinders' (358^{b}9, 359^{b}7), and the two sometimes appear to be used interchangeably, as in 357^{a}31–32 and 357^{b}2 and in *Probl.* 25, 8. 938^{b}25. Hesychius gives σποδός as a synonym for both. τέφρα was probably coarser and less pure than κονία. Hence κυκησίτεφρος κονία is supplied by the dishonest bathman in Aristophanes, *Frogs* 713.

(2) Lye, an alkaline fluid made by pouring water through ashes (384^{a}13, 389^{a}10, 27; cf. Pollux 7. 40).

(3) Quicklime (Theophrastus, *De Lap.*, §§ 9 and 68).

is the cause of all "fossiles" '. But neither draws attention to the significance of his rendering.

[1] Olympiodorus (op. cit., p. 269. 4) takes ἐκπυροῦσα as equivalent to ἐκπυρουμένη καὶ περιφρυττομένη, i.e. the dry exhalation forms the 'fossiles' 'by being burnt and parched'. This implies that the dry exhalation is the material cause of the 'fossiles' and is an obvious travesty of Aristotle's language. It is just possible, however, that Olympiodorus had not completely made up his mind as to the true solution. Compare an earlier remark of his, ὑπὸ μὲν γὰρ τῆς καπνώδους ἀναθυμιάσεως γίνεται τὰ καλούμενα ὑπὸ Ἀριστοτέλους Ὀρυκτά (op. cit., p. 266. 5–6), where ὑπό, strictly interpreted, must mean that the dry exhalation is the efficient cause.

[2] Generally speaking, regular verbs in -όω are transitive.

Of these (2) can be rejected at once because the 'fossiles' are not liquid, while (3) is not likely to be correct because the quicklime grows hot when it is moistened, whereas the 'fossiles' do not. We are left with (1). In this case, κονία κεχρωματισμένη must be coloured powder-ash, into which the raw material of the 'fossiles', presumably earth, is transformed by the heat and fire coming from the dry exhalation.

This interpretation of ἐκπυροῦσα and κονία κεχρωματισμένη is supported by an earlier passage (359^{b}4 ff.), which seems to have been neglected in this connexion. Here Aristotle is discussing the origin of salt streams and springs. 'Most of these, we must suppose, were once hot. Then the fire originally in them was extinguished, but the earth through which they percolate still remains like ashes and cinders (οἷον κονίαν καὶ τέφραν). There exist in many places springs and streams with all kinds of flavours, and the cause of all these flavours must be the fire that is or was present (reading ἐγγενομένην with Webster). For according as earth is burnt in a greater or a lesser degree, so it takes on every conceivable kind and shade of flavour (καομένη γὰρ ἡ γῆ τῷ μᾶλλον καὶ ἧττον παντοδαπὰς λαμβάνει μορφὰς καὶ χροὰς χυμῶν, 359^{b}10–12). It becomes full of στυπτηρία (alum) and κονία (here possibly potash) and other substances of the kind; and the fresh water which percolates through them is changed in character.'

Several important points should be noticed:

(1) The process occurs underground (for the waters percolate, διηθοῦνται), and this is where the formation of 'fossiles' takes place.

(2) Here earth is reduced by fire into a kind of κονία καὶ τέφρα. Compare with this κονία κεχρωματισμένη. It is true that fire, and not the dry exhalation, is the agent in this passage, but there is no inconsistency since, as we have already seen (p. 44), the dry exhalation is the source of the fire which exists within the earth.

(3) In this passage, earth exposed to fire in varying degrees assumes every kind of flavour. In the 'fossiles' passage the emphasis is not on flavour but on colour (κεχρωματισμένη). This is only natural, because most of the 'fossiles' mentioned by name are in fact brightly coloured and were used in painting.[1] May not Aristotle have supposed

[1] Realgar, ochre, ruddle, and cinnabar. See Theophr. *De Lap.*, §§ 50, 51, 58.

that exposure to fire causes earth to assume not only various flavours but also various colours?

Looked at in this way, the two passages supplement each other. The fire and heat from the dry exhalation form the 'fossiles' by reducing earth to the consistency of fine ash and perhaps causing it (although this is less certain) to take on bright colours. Those of the 'fossiles' which are stones must furthermore have been hardened by this heat ($383^{b}10$ ff.). This is as far as the evidence allows us to go.

Elsewhere in the *Meteorologica* ($384^{b}30$–34) there is a statement which might appear to contradict this view: 'Thus homogeneous bodies, both in plants and animals, and likewise the metals (τὰ μεταλλευόμενα), such as gold, silver, and the rest, are composed of water and earth—that is, water and earth and the exhalations from each of them when they are trapped underground (τῆς ἀναθυμιάσεως τῆς ἑκατέρου ἐγκατακλειομένης), as has been said elsewhere.'

Alexander (op. cit., p. 213. 16 ff.) takes τὰ μεταλλευόμενα in this passage as equivalent to 'metals and fossiles', and explains in accordance with the view he has already expressed that the former are composed of the moist exhalation (which is true) and the latter of the dry exhalation (which seems unlikely).[1] Alexander may perhaps have thought that τὰ μεταλλευόμενα here include the 'fossiles', just as they conceivably, but by no means certainly, include λίθος in $388^{a}13$ ff. But there is no reason to accept Alexander's interpretation, since the metals proper are in fact composed of both exhalations, the moist being combined with a proportion of the dry.

Our conclusion that the dry exhalation is the efficient, and not the material, cause of Aristotle's 'fossiles' seems to be corroborated by Theophrastus. In *De Lap.*, § 50, he discusses a group of mineral earths, of which three, namely ochre, ruddle, and realgar, are cited by Aristotle as 'fossiles'. In describing their origin Theophrastus states that '*some of them* at least have obviously undergone exposure to fire (πεπυρωμένα) and some process of complete combustion, as, for example, realgar, orpiment, and the like, but it may be stated generally that *all* are products of the dry and smoky exhalation' (πάντα δ' ὡς ἁπλῶς εἰπεῖν ἀπὸ τῆς ἀναθυμιάσεως

---

[1] Olympiodorus (op. cit., p. 314. 18 ff.) does not commit himself.

ταῦτα τῆς ξηρᾶς καὶ καπνώδους). The phrasing of the last sentence, ἀπὸ τῆς ἀναθυμιάσεως, at first sight suggests that the exhalation is conceived as the material cause of these earths. But if the statement is taken as a whole this interpretation is precluded. The argument runs: '*Some* of these earths show clear evidence of having been burnt (cf. πεπυρωμένα with Aristotle's ἐκπυροῦσα), but as a matter of fact *all* ⟨have been exposed to fire since *all*⟩ are products of the dry exhalation.' This makes sense only if the dry exhalation is the efficient cause in the formation of these earths. Moreover, had Theophrastus' opinion of the matter differed radically from Aristotle's, there can be little doubt that he would have drawn attention to the fact. This he is careful to do in dealing with another aspect of Aristotle's theory, namely, the suggestion that most of the 'fossils' are coloured κονία. According to Theophrastus, only some of the coloured earths are composed of κονία; others are composed of sand, and others just of earth (*De Lap.*, § 40).

But even clearer support for our conclusion comes, surprisingly enough, from Georgius Agricola, the sixteenth-century mineralogist, who made determined efforts to interpret and correct the theories of Aristotle and Theophrastus in the light of his own practical knowledge. His verdict is: 'non videtur autem exhalatio sicca esse materia terrarum quae in venis et venulis gignuntur; sed potius ignita terras immutare atque eo modo novas species gignere potest.'[1] Agricola no doubt thought that he was correcting Aristotle; he would have been pleased to find that he was corroborating him.

MANUSCRIPTS AND EDITIONS

A. *Manuscripts*

The lettering adopted in this edition was proposed by Nigel Wilson (*Classical Philology*, lvi (1961), 109). This differs from that of Fobes (Theophrastus, *Metaphysics*, ed. W. D. Ross and F. H. Fobes, Oxford, 1929, pp. xxvi–xxvii, xxxiii). The dating for the most part is that indicated by Wilson in his article and in correspondence. Dating by watermarks is not entirely accurate, and

[1] Georgius Agricola, *De Re Metallica*, Libri xii, Basle, 1657; *De Ortu et Causis Subterraneorum*, iii, p. 508. Agricola lived 1490-1555.

when such dates are given, it is best to allow a margin of fifteen years in either direction.

Sigla

A   Vaticanus graecus 1302 (Fobes A), late 13th–14th century.[1]
B   Vaticanus graecus 1305 (Fobes V), *c.* 1469–77.[1] Ends in § 43.
C   Vaticanus Urbinas graecus 108 (Fobes Va), 15th century (Fobes).
D   Vaticanus Palatinus graecus 162 (Fobes R), 1442–59 (Wilson).
E   Vaticanus Ottobonianus graecus 153 (Fobes O), 15th century (Wilson).
     Ends in § 67.
F   Vaticanus Reginensis graecus 123 (Fobes u), watermark of *c.* 1499–1501
     (Wilson).
G   Ambrosianus P. 80 sup. (Fobes D), 15th century (Fobes and Wilson).
H   Neapolitanus III D 1 (not used by Fobes), 1497 (Wilson). Ends in § 43.
J   Marcianus graecus 260 (Fobes M), 1442–59 (apparently by the same
     hand as D).
K   Bernensis 402 (Fobes B), 15th century (Fobes and Wilson).
L   Vossianus graecus Q25 (Fobes H), watermark of *c.* 1487 (Wilson).
M   Londiniensis, Brit. Mus. Add. 5113 (Fobes S), watermark of *c.* 1480–7
     (Wilson).
N   Parisinus graecus 2277 (Fobes z), watermark of *c.* 1479 (Wilson).

Manuscripts ABC were collated for the present edition some years ago. After his own edition had been published in 1956, John F. C. Richards ascertained the existence of D,[2] and this too was collated. More recently Nigel Wilson discovered that eight of the manuscripts[3] used by Fobes in editing the *Metaphysics* included, among other works, the text of the *De Lapidibus*. Finally both Richards and Wilson found a reference to yet another manuscript (H) in the catalogue of the Naples Library. Professor Richards obtained photographs of the nine freshly discovered manuscripts, and kindly made them available so that the present collation might be complete.[4]

Hopes that one or other of the nine new manuscripts might represent a better tradition than that of those previously known were not fulfilled. All thirteen manuscripts belong to the same family, for all show the same lacunae in §§ 8, 20, 21, 23, 27, and 43.

[1] Nigel Wilson in a letter of 5 June 1961. He notes that B has a watermark (no. 5910 in Briquet) which points to the dates mentioned.

[2] J. F. C. Richards, 'Heinsius and a manuscript of Theophrastus', *Classical Philology*, liv (1959), 118–19.

[3] Now lettered EFGJKLMN.

[4] See also J. F. C. Richards, 'Nine New Manuscripts of Theophrastus *On Stones*', *Classical Philology*, lviii (1963), 34–36. He does not attempt a stemma.

FKLM form a group; for example, § 28, καὶ τῆς . . . ξηρότατον *om.* FKLM; § 21, αὖ] αὖ καὶ FKLM.

F (*c.* 1499–1501) appears to have been copied from Aldus (1495), or at least from a manuscript used by Aldus, all of whose errors it shares, while adding others of its own in §§ 8, 51, and 53. Errors are shared by L with Aldus (and F) in §§ 47 and 56, and so too is a correct reading in § 63. Aldus may have copied a corrected version of a manuscript similar to L.

Each member of the group FKLM contains individual errors of its own; K in § 33, and L in §§ 25 and 37, while M has omissions in §§ 1, 15, and 26. F has the errors in §§ 8, 51, and 53 that have been mentioned, apart from others shared with Aldus but with no manuscript. K and M each have some correct readings not found in other manuscripts. F has one correct reading not shared by Aldus: this occurs in § 69 and seems to have been achieved accidentally by the omission of τό. L has no correct readings of its own whatsoever. L fails to share correct readings with FKM in §§ 1, 6, 10, 23, 53, and 58, so that FKM are virtually a sub-group of their own, since L has considerably more mistakes.

In the group ABCDEGHJN, CE form a sub-group; for example, § 8, σπάνιοι] σπανίοις CE; § 62, ἀλιπὲς] ἐλλιπὲς C: ἐλλειπὲς E. E has many individual mistakes and omissions; for example, § 24, ἀνακεῖσθαι . . . πηχῶν *om.* E. It also offers sound readings not found in other manuscripts, for example, § 25, ἰδιωτέρως; § 29, ἄγουσα; § 45, ἀλλοιοῦν; § 47, τὸ δοκιμάζειν; § 67, ὑφαιρουμένη. Turnebus has the first and third of these, but not the second, fourth, and, above all, the last. His partial agreement with E may be fortuitous, as may be that of Furlanus with K² in § 53 (πανδοχείου).

Although A is considerably the oldest of the manuscripts, no others seem to have been copied from it. It alone preserves certain correct readings; for example, in § 29 (ἀκολουθοίη for ἀκολουθείη) and in § 31 (ὁ ἄρρην for ὁ ἄρρεν). G has an individual mistake in § 64 (περεκίαν). N contains several individual mistakes (in §§ 1, 19, 24, &c.) and an individual lacuna (§ 63, διαφοραὶ . . . Σάμῳ).

N also shares the omission of μάλιστα . . . ἱμάτια in § 64 with DJ. But this may be a coincidence: a lacuna could easily have arisen at this point because of the occurrence of the phrase πρὸς τὰ ἱμάτια in two successive sentences. Moreover, N does not share the errors of DJ in §§ 4 (μάραγδος) and 23 (μὲν οὖν). DJ, as we shall see, are more closely linked with BH, which do not share the lacuna in § 64 because they cease in § 43. The affiliation is shown by § 22, πολυτιμοτέρα ACEGN: πολυτιμότερον FKLM: πολυτιμότερος BDHJ.

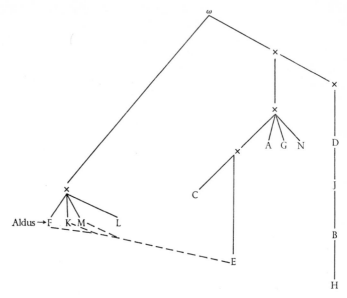

D and J seem to be by the same hand. That J is a copy of D is indicated by § 58, κόκκος] κρόκκος D: κρόκος J, where κρόκος ('saffron') seems to be a crude attempt to make sense of the *vox nihili* κρόκκος. B, as Fobes saw, is copied from J. This is confirmed by § 30, ἔμφασιν] ἔμφεισιν BH, where B was misled by J's writing, and again by § 31, οἴνωπον] οἴνοπον B²HJ (οἴνοππον B¹). H is almost certainly a fair-copy of B, as can be seen from § 24, σμαράγδους B²H (*νους ceteri*), and from § 33, τὸ λευκὸν χλωροειδέστερον B²H (*lacunam pro λευκὸν ceteri*). H has an individual omission in § 15. The line of descent is illustrated by § 35, τῆς Βακτριανῆς] τῆς Βακτριανοῖς DJ: τοῖς Βακτριανοῖς BH, although the importance of this example should not be over-estimated, since the pronunciation of all three readings would have been identical for a medieval or Renaissance scribe.

BH end at παρά (*sic*) in § 43 and continue with *De Sudore* § 19.

Since in J παρα occurs at the very end of a verso page, B's scribe, while copying J, probably failed to keep his place when he resumed his work after a break.

E shows contamination with the FKLM group, or at least with FKM, and particularly with F. Among several examples are § 1, χρώμασιν EFK²M; § 49, ὥς τινές EFK²; § 66, ἡ ἰσχύς EF. The stemma which seems to result from this discussion is shown on p. 50.

B. Editions

Abbreviations

Aldus	*Aristoteles et Theophrastus*, vol. ii, Venice, 1497 (editio princeps).
Turnebus (text)	*Theophrasti Lib. De Lapidibus, ex officina Federici Morelli*, Paris, 1577.
Turnebus (translation)	*Theophrasti De Lapidibus Liber, ab Adriano Turnebo Latinitate donatus, ex officina Federici Morelli*, Paris, 1578.
Furlanus	*Theophrasti Eresii . . . pleraque*, ed. D. Furlanus, Hanau, 1605. (Text and Latin translation.)
Heinsius	*Theophrasti Eresii Graece et Latine opera omnia*, ed. D. Heinsius, Leiden, 1613.
de Laet	*Theophrasti Liber De Lapidibus*, ed. J. de Laet, Leiden, 1647. (Text, Latin translation, and short notes, forming part of the third edition of A. de Boodt, *Gemmarum et Lapidum Historia*.)
Hill	*Theophrastus's History of Stones*, by John Hill, 1st edition, London, 1746; 2nd edition, London, 1774. (Text, English translation, and notes.)
Schneider	*Theophrasti Eresii opera quae supersunt omnia*, ed. J. G. Schneider, vols. i–iv, Leipzig, 1818; vol. v, Leipzig, 1821. (Text of the *De Lapidibus* in vol. i; Latin translation (that of Turnebus) in vol. ii; notes in vol. iv; supplementary notes in vol. v.)
Wimmer (Teubner)	*Theophrasti Eresii opera quae supersunt omnia*, rec. F. Wimmer, vol. iii, Teubner, Leipzig, 1862.
Wimmer (Didot)	*Theophrasti Eresii opera quae supersunt omnia*, ed. F. Wimmer, Firmin Didot, Paris, 1866. (Text and Latin translation.)
Caley & Richards	*Theophrastus, On Stones; Introduction, Greek Text, English Translation and Commentary*, by Earle R. Caley and John F. C. Richards, Columbus, 1956.

The first printed text of the *De Lapidibus* appeared in 1497 as part of vol. ii of the Aldine edition of Aristotle and Theophrastus. This text was reprinted in the Basle edition of Oporinus in 1541, and in the Aldine edition of Camotius in 1552. The first separate text of the work, issued by Morel at Paris in 1577, was a vast improvement on that of the previous editions. Indeed, for nearly 250 years it remained the best of those available. Although it does not bear Turnebus's name, it must have been edited under his supervision since the admirable emendations that it contains are followed in his translation, which was printed in the following year. Both the text and the translation must have been prepared some years earlier for Turnebus had died in 1565. Further emendations are indicated in the translation.

Unfortunately Turnebus's work was slighted by Furlanus, whose emendations, sometimes sound but frequently unsound, were reproduced by Heinsius, de Laet, and Hill. The improvements introduced by de Laet were mostly taken from the notes of Salmasius.[1] Hill's text and translation are less valuable than his commentary, which was based on a wide knowledge of the natural science of his time. His edition of the *De Lapidibus* brought him money and fame, but his most important work, a massive botanical treatise in twenty-four folio volumes entitled 'A Complete Vegetable System', earned him the Swedish Order of the Polar Star; and this honour prompted Hill to usurp another, that of a knighthood. At one time he sold medical prescriptions, among them a sovereign remedy for gout, the complaint of which he died. Hill's English version of the *De Lapidibus* was translated anonymously into French (1754), and into German by A. H. Baumgärtner (1770) and apparently by C. Schmieder (1807).[2]

Schneider, in preparing his text, wisely reverted to Turnebus and printed some of the emendations indicated in Turnebus's translation, which he reissued. He studied also manuscript L, but copied it carelessly. When he wrote his supplementary notes (vol. v), he had before him a collation of manuscripts ABC, but of this he made little use. He noted, however, a few valuable emendations that had been proposed by Coraës. Schneider's chief fault was excessive zeal, and some of his clumsier emendations were rightly rejected by Wimmer. Otherwise, Wimmer in his two virtually identical texts closely followed Schneider, and did not

---

[1] Claudius Salmasius (Claude de Saumaise), *Plinianae Exercitationes*, Paris, 1629 (Utrecht, 1689).

[2] F. D. Adams (*The Birth and Development of the Geological Sciences*, Baltimore, 1938, p. 21) states that Schmieder's version is a translation of Hill's, but verification has not been possible since the book is rare.

examine any manuscripts. His editing of the Greek was intended to be conservative, but inaccuracies sometimes prevent it from achieving even this modest aim. Apart from minor omissions, he omits, like Schneider, a whole sentence in § 68. Wimmer's texts were the basis of versions by F. de Mély (1902) and K. Mieleitner (1922).[1] In 1896 a translation into modern Greek with brief notes was published by M. K. Stephanides.[1]

The edition of Caley and Richards, published in 1956, marks a notable advance, particularly in respect of its mineralogical notes. The textual apparatus is also valuable in that it contains an admirable collation of manuscripts ABC and a full list of emendations dating from Aldus down to the present day. But apart from some corrections and a few new emendations, the text adopted is that of Wimmer. This procedure, for which perhaps the editors are not to blame, has left many unsolved difficulties lurking in the text and in the translation.

Although ten manuscripts, as well as ABC, have been collated for the present edition, the results have been disappointing. Most of the important errors and omissions were found to be repeated. Wherever possible, however, manuscript readings have been restored, and several passages have been emended with their help, and in some cases with the aid of parallel passages from Theophrastus and other authors. One lacuna, in § 33, has been repaired with a reading adopted from BH, for although these manuscripts, as the stemma shows (p. 50), have no authority, the reading in question is at least no worse than the emendation since proposed. Elsewhere, tentative stopgaps have been provided. In §§ 40 and 53, sentences have been transferred to other sections. The expedients adopted in §§ 43 and 57 are the most drastic and the least satisfactory. In many instances previous emendations and conjectures have been carefully considered, and some have been admitted or readmitted to the text if, without doing violence to the manuscript evidence, they alone make reasonable sense.

[1] See the Bibliography, pp. 134 ff.

NOTE

In addition to those listed on p. 51, the following abbreviations are used in the apparatus criticus:

codd.	the consensus of manuscripts.
ceteri	the other manuscripts.
edd.	previous editors.
Schneider (in suppl.)	J. G. Schneider, *Theophrasti Eresii opera quae supersunt omnia*, vol. v, 1821.
Schneider, &c.	Schneider, Wimmer, Caley and Richards.
C.P.	Theophrastus, *de Causis Plantarum*.
H.P.	Theophrastus, *Historia Plantarum*.

Manuscripts BHJ are not usually cited unless their readings are significant. Some minor variants found in other manuscripts have also been omitted.

TEXT

ΠΕΡΙ ΛΙΘΩΝ

1 **I.** Τῶν ἐν τῇ γῇ συνισταμένων τὰ μέν ἐστιν ὕδατος, τὰ δὲ γῆς. ὕδατος μὲν τὰ μεταλλευόμενα καθάπερ ἄργυρος καὶ χρυσὸς καὶ τἆλλα, γῆς δὲ λίθος τε καὶ ὅσα λίθων εἴδη περιττότερα, καὶ εἴ τινες δὴ τῆς γῆς αὐτῆς ἰδιώτεραι φύσεις εἰσὶν ἢ χρώμασιν ἢ λειότησιν ἢ πυκνότησιν ἢ καὶ ἄλλῃ τινὶ δυνάμει. περὶ μὲν οὖν τῶν μεταλλευομένων ἐν ἄλλοις 2 τεθεώρηται· περὶ δὲ τούτων νῦν λέγωμεν. ἅπαντα οὖν ταῦτα χρὴ νομίζειν ὡς ἁπλῶς εἰπεῖν ἐκ καθαρᾶς τινος συνεστάναι καὶ ὁμαλῆς ὕλης, εἴτε συρροῆς εἴτε διηθήσεώς τινος γινομένης, εἴτε ὡς ἀνωτέρω εἴρηται καὶ κατ᾽ ἄλλον τρόπον ἐκκεκριμένης· τάχα γὰρ ἐνδέχεται τὰ μὲν οὕτως, τὰ δ᾽ ἐκείνως, τὰ δ᾽ ἄλλως. ἀφ᾽ ὧν δὴ καὶ τὸ λεῖον καὶ τὸ πυκνὸν καὶ τὸ στιλπνὸν καὶ διαφανὲς καὶ τἆλλα τὰ τοιαῦτα ἔχουσι, καὶ ὅσῳ ἂν καὶ ὁμαλεστέρων καὶ καθαρωτέρων ἕκαστον ᾖ τοσούτῳ καὶ ταῦτα μᾶλλον ὑπάρχει. τὸ γὰρ ὅλον ὡς ἂν ἀκριβείας ἔχῃ τὰ κατὰ τὴν 3 σύστασιν ἢ πῆξιν οὕτως ἀκολουθεῖ καὶ τὰ ἀπ᾽ ἐκείνων. ἡ δὲ πῆξις τοῖς μὲν ἀπὸ θερμοῦ τοῖς δ᾽ ἀπὸ ψυχροῦ γίνεται. κωλύει γὰρ ἴσως οὐδὲν ἔνια γένη λίθων ὑφ᾽ ἑκατέρων συνίστασθαι τούτων. ἐπεὶ τά γε τῆς γῆς ἅπαντα δόξειεν ἂν ὑπὸ πυρός· ἐπείπερ ἐν τοῖς ἐναντίοις ἑκάστων ἡ πῆξις καὶ ἡ τῆξις. ἰδιότητες δὲ πλείους εἰσὶν ἐν τοῖς λίθοις· ἐν γὰρ τῇ γῇ χρώμασί τε καὶ γλισχρότητι καὶ λειότητι καὶ πυκνότητι 4 καὶ τοῖς τοιούτοις αἱ πολλαὶ διαφοραί, κατὰ δὲ τὰ ἄλλα σπάνιοι. τοῖς δὲ λίθοις αἵ τ᾽ αὐταὶ καὶ πρὸς ταῖς τοιαύταις αἱ κατὰ τὰς δυνάμεις τοῦ τε ποιεῖν ἢ πάσχειν καὶ τοῦ μὴ πάσχειν. τηκτοὶ γὰρ οἱ δ᾽ ἄτηκτοι, καὶ καυστοὶ οἱ δ᾽ ἄκαυστοι, καὶ ἄλλα τούτοις ὅμοια, καὶ ἐν αὐτῇ τῇ καύσει

1 εἴδη om. M Furlanus.   φύσεις] φύσις N.   χρώμασιν EFK²M: χρώμενα ceteri.
καὶ ἄλλῃ] καὶ om. Schneider, &c.   λέγωμεν FK²M: λέγομεν ceteri.   2 οὖν F
Aldus: δὲ E: ἂν ceteri.   συρροῆς Wimmer (coni. Schneider): ῥοῆς codd.   τινος Wimmer:
διά τινος codd.: διά in uncis posuit Schneider.   γινομένης codd.: γενομένης Schneider,
&c.   ὡς ἀνωτέρω εἴρηται EF: ἀνωτέρως εἴρηται ceteri.   καὶ κατ᾽] καὶ om. C.
καὶ ὁμαλεστέρων ACDEGKLMN (καὶ om. N): καὶ ὁμαλέστερον F Aldus (καὶ om.
Schneider, &c.).   καθαρωτέρων ACDEGKLMN: καθαρώτερον F edd.   τὸ γὰρ
ὅλον] τὸ ὅλον A, fortasse recte; cf. § 40.   τὰ κατὰ Schneider: τε κατὰ codd.   3 τά
γε Turnebus: τά τε codd.   δόξειεν ἂν Turnebus: δόξειαν E: δόξειεν ceteri.   ἐπείπερ
ἐν Turnebus: ἐπείπερ E Schneider, &c.: ἐπεῖπεν N: ἐπείπερ ἂν ceteri codd.   ἐν γὰρ]
ἐν μὲν γὰρ Turnebus.   αἱ πολλαὶ διαφοραί Turnebus: αἱ *αἱ διαφοραὶ E: αἱ πνοαὶ
διάφοροι ceteri codd.: αἱ ῥοαὶ διάφοροι Furlanus.   4 αἵ τ᾽ αὐταὶ ego: ἅπτεται codd.:
αὐταί τε Turnebus.   ταῖς τοιαύταις ego: ταῖς ἑαυταῖς codd.: ταύταις Turnebus.   τοῦ
τε Turnebus: οὕτε codd.   καὶ τοῦ ego: ἢ τοῦ codd., edd.

TRANSLATION

ON STONES

I. 1. Of the things that are formed within the earth, some are of
water and some of earth. Of water are metals, like silver, gold, and
the rest; while of earth are stone, including the more unusual
kinds, and those varieties of earth that are at all peculiar in
colour, smoothness, solidity, or some other quality. Metals, however, have been considered elsewhere, and it is the latter that we
have now to discuss. 2. Generally speaking, we must suppose
that all these latter things are formed of a pure and uniform
matter, this matter being produced as a result either of a 'conflux' or of 'filtering' or, as has been explained above, of some
other process of separation: some of this matter may possibly
be produced by the one process, some by the other, and some
in yet a different way. It is from this matter, to be sure, that
stones and earths derive smoothness, solidity, lustre, transparency, and other qualities of this kind, qualities which are present in a varying degree according to the purity and uniformity
of the matter of which each of the stones or earths is composed.
For in general it is the perfection, greater or less, of the matter
subjected to composition or solidification that directly deter-
mines the qualities derived from that matter. 3. This solidification is due in some cases to heat and in others to cold, for there
may be nothing to prevent certain kinds of stone from being
formed either by heat or by cold; although it would seem that the
earths at any rate are all formed by fire, since the process whereby
a thing is solidified and the process whereby it suffers dissolution
belong to contrary *genera*. As for peculiarities, these are more
numerous in stones than in the earths. Indeed, so far as the earths
are concerned, most of the characteristic differences are in respect
of colour, viscidity, smoothness, solidity, and the like: differences
in other respects are rare. 4. Stones, however, while possessing
these same differences, have, in addition to such differences,
others in respect of their capacity (*a*) to act on other substances,
or (*b*) to react to them, and to fail so to react. For instance,
(*b*) some stones can be melted while others cannot be, some are
combustible while others are not, and so forth. Moreover, in the

58 THEOPHRASTUS

καὶ πυρώσει πλείους ἔχοντες διαφοράς. ἔνιοι δὲ τοῖς χρώμασιν ἐξομοιοῦσθαι δύνανται τὸ ὕδωρ ὥσπερ ἡ σμάραγδος, οἱ δ' ὅλως ἀπολιθοῦν τὰ τιθέμενα εἰς ἑαυτούς, ἕτεροι δ' ὁλκήν τινα ποιεῖν, οἱ δὲ βασανίζειν τὸν χρυσὸν καὶ τὸν ἄργυρον ὥσπερ ἥ τε καλουμένη λίθος Ἡρακλεία 5 καὶ ἡ Λυδή. θαυμασιωτάτη δὲ καὶ μεγίστη δύναμις, εἴπερ ἀληθές, ἡ τῶν τικτόντων· γνωριμωτέρα δὲ τούτων καὶ ἐν πλείοσιν ⟨ἡ⟩ κατὰ τὰς ἐργασίας· γλυπτοὶ γὰρ ἔνιοι καὶ τορνευτοὶ καὶ πριστοί, τῶν δὲ οὐδὲ ὅλως ἅπτεται σιδήριον, ἐνίων δὲ κακῶς καὶ μόλις. εἰσὶ δὲ πλείους 6 καὶ ἄλλαι κατὰ ταύτας ⟨διαφοραί⟩. αἱ μὲν οὖν κατὰ τὰ χρώματα καὶ τὰς σκληρότητας καὶ μαλακότητας καὶ λειότητας καὶ τἆλλα τὰ τοιαῦτα, δι' ὧν τὸ περιττόν, πλείοσιν ὑπάρχουσι καὶ ἐνίοις γε κατὰ τόπον ὅλον. ἐξ ὧν δὴ καὶ διωνομασμέναι λιθοτομίαι Παρίων τε καὶ Πεντελικῶν καὶ Χίων τε καὶ Θηβαϊκῶν, καὶ ὡς ὁ περὶ Αἴγυπτον ἐν Θήβαις ἀλαβαστρίτης,—καὶ γὰρ οὗτος μέγας τέμνεται,—καὶ ὁ τῷ ἐλέφαντι ὅμοιος ὁ χερνίτης καλούμενος, ἐν ᾗ πυέλῳ φασὶ καὶ Δαρεῖον κεῖσθαι· 7 καὶ ὁ πόρος ὅμοιος τῷ χρώματι καὶ τῇ πυκνότητι τῷ Παρίῳ τὴν δὲ κουφότητα μόνον ἔχων τοῦ πόρου, διὸ καὶ ἐν τοῖς σπουδαζομένοις οἰκήμασιν ὥσπερ διάζωμα τιθέασιν αὐτὸν οἱ Αἰγύπτιοι· καὶ μέλας αὐτόθι διαφανὴς ὁμοίως τῷ Χίῳ, καὶ παρ' ἄλλοις δὲ ἕτεροι πλείους. αἱ μὲν οὖν τοιαῦται διαφοραὶ καθάπερ ἐλέχθη κοινότεραι πλείοσιν, αἱ δὲ κατὰ τὰς δυνάμεις τὰς προειρημένας οὐκέτι τόποις ὅλοις ὑπάρ-8 χουσιν οὐδὲ συνεχείαις λίθων οὐδὲ μεγέθεσιν. ἔνιοι δὲ καὶ σπάνιοι πάμπαν εἰσὶ καὶ σμικροὶ καθάπερ ἥ τε σμάραγδος καὶ τὸ σάρδιον καὶ ὁ ἄνθραξ καὶ ἡ σάπφειρος καὶ σχεδὸν οἱ ἐν λόγῳ τῶν εἰς τὰ σφραγίδια γλυπτῶν. οἱ δὲ καὶ ἐν ἑτέροις εὑρίσκονται διακοπτομένοις. ὀλίγοι δὲ καὶ οἱ περὶ τὴν πύρωσιν καὶ καῦσιν, ὑπὲρ ὧν δὴ καὶ πρῶτον ἴσως λεκτέον τίνας καὶ πόσας ἔχουσι διαφοράς.

4 ἐξομοιοῦσθαι δύνανται ego; cf. § 23, ἐξομοιοῦται: ἐξομοιοῦνται (ἐξομοιοῦται C) δυνάμενοι codd.: ἐξομοιοῦν φαίνονται δυνάμενοι Turnebus: ἐξομοιοῦν λέγονται δυνάμενοι Furlanus, Schneider: ἐξομοιοῦν[ται] δυνάμενοι Caley & Richards. σμάραγδος] μάραγδος BDHJ. 5 τικτόντων Schneider: τηκτῶν EFK² Aldus: τικτῶν ceteri. τούτων καὶ ego: *τῶν καὶ E: καὶ τῶν BH: τῶν καὶ ceteri: τῶν in uncis posuit Schneider. ἐν πλείοσιν ⟨ἡ⟩ coni. Schneider: ἐν πλείοσι codd. ἄλλαι E: ἄλλα ceteri. κατὰ ταύτας ⟨διαφοραί⟩ Turnebus (in versione), Furlanus: lacunam post κατὰ ταύτας codd.: lacunam post παρὰ ταύτας Turnebus (in textu): παρὰ ταύτας διαφοραί Schneider. 6 δι' ὧν τὸ περιττόν ACDEGN: διὸ τὸ περιττόν FKLM: διὰ τὸ περιττόν Furlanus. ὅλον B(?) EH: ὅλου ceteri. Θηβαϊκῶν FK²M: θηραϊκῶν ceteri. ἀλαβαστρίτης B²FHK²M: λαβαστρίτης ceteri. οὗτος] οὕτως N. ὅμοιος Turnebus: ὅμολος B²HK²: μόνος ceteri. πυέλῳ coni. Salmasius: πέπλῳ codd. 7 ὅμοιος] ὅμος N. μόνον om. E. καὶ μέλας Wimmer: lacunam ante μέλας codd. ὁμοίως ACEFKM: ὁμοίω B¹DGJLN: ὅμοιος B²H Schneider, Caley & Richards. πλείους B²EH: lacunam post πλει (πλ L) ceteri. τοιαῦται] τοιαῦτα EF Aldus. τόποις ὅλοις coni. Schneider:

very process of combustion or, rather, of exposure to fire stones exhibit many differences. Again, (*a*) some stones, the *smaragdus* for example, have the power of communicating their colour to water, and others that of completely petrifying objects placed in them. Some have a power of attraction, and others that of testing gold and silver, like the so-called 'Heraclean' and 'Lydian' stones. 5. But the greatest and most remarkable power, if this is true, is that possessed by the stones which bring forth other stones. What is more familiar than these capacities and more frequent in its occurrence is that which concerns the working of stones. For some can be carved or turned on a lathe or sawn, while on others an iron tool makes only a poor and slight impression, and on others no impression whatsoever. There are many other differences in regard to the working of stones. 6. Numerous stones, then, possess characteristic differences in respect of colour, hardness, softness, smoothness, and other such qualities which cause them to be exceptional. Moreover, in some cases at least, these differences belong to the stone of a whole region. As instances, there are of course the celebrated quarries of Paros, Pentelicus, Chios, and the Thebaid; there is the *alabastrites*, which likewise is hewn in large pieces, being found near the Egyptian Thebes, and a stone like ivory known as the 'chernites', in a coffin of which Darius is said to be buried. 7. Again, there is the (Egyptian) *poros*, which is similar to Parian marble in colour and compactness, and possesses merely the lightness of ordinary *poros*: hence the Egyptians use it for courses in their fine buildings. There is found in Egypt, moreover, a black stone, transparent like that of Chios, and many others elsewhere. Numerous stones, then, partake of characteristic differences such as these, as was stated above. On the other hand, those differences previously described which stones possess in virtue of the capacity to act or react do not similarly belong (*a*) to a whole region, or (*b*) to continuous masses of stone, or (*c*) to stones of great size. 8. In fact, some of the stones to which they belong are (*a*) very rare and (*c*) small, for example the *smaragdus*, the 'sard', the *anthrax*, the *sapphirus*, and indeed almost all the stones that rank among those carved into signets. And some are (*b*) actually found inside other stones when these are split. The stones which have to do with burning and combustion also are few in number; and it is the characteristic differences of these stones that we should perhaps first describe and enumerate.

τοῖς ὅλοις (ἄλλοις M) *codd.*   8 ἔνιοι FLM: ἐνίοις *ceteri.* σπάνιοι] σπανίοις CE.
οἱ ἐν λόγῳ τῶν *ego: lacunam ante* λόγον *codd., Wimmer.*   σφραγίδια] σφραγίδα F.

9 **II.** Κατὰ δὴ τὴν πύρωσιν οἱ μὲν τήκονται καὶ ῥέουσιν ὥσπερ οἱ μεταλλευτοί. ῥεῖ γὰρ ἅμα τῷ ἀργύρῳ καὶ τῷ χαλκῷ καὶ σιδήρῳ καὶ ἡ λίθος ἡ ἐκ τούτων, εἴτ᾽ οὖν διὰ τὴν ὑγρότητα τῶν ἐνυπαρχόντων εἴτε καὶ δι᾽ αὑτούς· ὡσαύτως δὲ καὶ οἱ πυρομάχοι καὶ οἱ μυλίαι συρρέουσιν οἷς ἐπιτιθέασιν οἱ καίοντες. οἱ δὲ καὶ ὅλως λέγουσι πάντας τήκεσθαι πλὴν τοῦ μαρμάρου, τοῦτον δὲ κατακαίεσθαι καὶ κονίαν ἐξ αὐτοῦ γίνεσθαι.

10 δόξειε δ᾽ ἂν οὕτως ὅλως ἐπὶ πλεῖον εἰρῆσθαι· πολλοὶ γὰρ οἱ ῥηγνύμενοι καὶ διαπηδῶντες ὡς ἀπομαχόμενοι τὴν πύρωσιν ὥσπερ οὐδ᾽ ὁ κέραμος. ὃ καὶ κατὰ λόγον ἐστίν, οἵτινες ἐξυγρασμένοι τυγχάνουσιν· τὸ γὰρ

11 τηκτὸν ἔνικμον εἶναι δεῖ καὶ ὑγρότητ᾽ ἔχειν πλείω. φασὶ δὲ καὶ τῶν ἡλιουμένων τοὺς μὲν ἀναξηραίνεσθαι τελείως ὥστ᾽ ἀχρείους εἶναι μὴ καταβρεχθέντας πάλιν καὶ συνικμασθέντας τοὺς δὲ καὶ μαλακωτέρους καὶ διαθραύστους μᾶλλον. φανερὸν δὲ ὡς ἀμφοτέρων μὲν ἐξαιρεῖται τὴν ὑγρότητα, συμβαίνει δὲ τοὺς μὲν πυκνοὺς ἀποξηραινομένους σκληρύνεσθαι, τοὺς δὲ μανοὺς καὶ ὧν ἡ σύμφυσις τοιαύτη θραυστοὺς

12 εἶναι καὶ κατακτούς. ἔνιοι δὲ τῶν θραυστῶν ἀνθρακοῦνται τῇ καύσει καὶ διαμένουσι πλείω χρόνον ὥσπερ οἱ περὶ Βίνας ἐν τῷ μετάλλῳ οὓς ὁ ποταμὸς καταφέρει· καίονται γὰρ ὅταν ἄνθρακες ἐπιτεθῶσι καὶ μέχρι τούτου ἄχρις ἂν φυσᾷ τις, εἶτ᾽ ἀπομαραίνονται καὶ πάλιν καίονται, διὸ καὶ πολὺν χρόνον ἡ χρῆσις· ἡ δ᾽ ὀσμὴ βαρεῖα σφόδρα καὶ δυσχερής.

13 ὃν δὲ καλοῦσι σπῖνον, ὃς ἦν ἐν τοῖς μετάλλοις τούτοις, οὗτος διακοπεὶς καὶ συντεθεὶς πρὸς ἑαυτὸν ἐν τῷ ἡλίῳ τιθέμενος καίεται, καὶ μᾶλλον

14 ἐὰν ἐπιψεκάσῃ καὶ περιρράνῃ τις. ὁ δὲ Λιπαραῖος ἐκπορούταί τε τῇ καύσει καὶ γίνεται κισσηροειδὴς ὥσθ᾽ ἅμα τήν τε χρόαν μεταβάλλειν καὶ τὴν πυκνότητα· μέλας τε γὰρ καὶ λεῖός ἐστι καὶ πυκνὸς ἄκαυστος ὤν. γίνεται δ᾽ οὗτος ἐν τῇ κισσήρει διειλημμένος ἄλλοθι καὶ ἄλλοθι καθάπερ ἐν χυτριδίῳ καὶ οὐ συνεχής, ὥσπερ καὶ ἐν Μήλῳ φασὶ τὴν κίσσηριν ἐν ἄλλῳ τινὶ λίθῳ γίνεσθαι. καὶ εἴη ἂν τούτῳ ὥσπερ

9 σιδήρῳ] τῷ σιδήρῳ M Schneider. εἴτ᾽ οὖν Schneider: εἴτε E: εἰ τοίνυν ceteri. ἐνυπαρχόντων Schneider: ὑπαρχόντων codd. δι᾽ αὑτούς Schneider: δι᾽ αὐτὰς aut δι᾽ αὐτὰς codd. μυλίαι Turnebus: μιλίαι codd. συρρέουσιν coni. Caley & Richards: ῥέουσιν codd. πάντας F edd.: πάντα ceteri. 10 ὅλως] ὅλος M: om. Wimmer, Caley & Richards. ἀπομαχόμενοι Schneider, &c.: οὐ μαχομένου (μαχουμένου M¹) codd.: οὐ μαχόμενοι ⟨κατὰ⟩ Furlanus. οὐδ᾽ ὁ] οὐδ᾽ οὐ E: οὐδ᾽ in uncis posuerunt Schneider, &c. ἐξυγρασμένοι FK²M: ἐξ. . .μενοι E: ἐξηγορασμένοι ceteri. τὸ γὰρ EF: ὁ γὰρ aut ὁ γὰρ ceteri. δεῖ Schneider: ἀεὶ codd. ἔχειν C²E Schneider: ἔχει ceteri. 11 καταβρεχθέντας Furlanus: καταρρηχθέντας codd. συνικμασθέντας AE: συνεκμασθέντας ceteri. καὶ ὧν EK²: καὶ ὡς ceteri. καὶ κατακτούς ego: καὶ τηκτούς AB²(?)EF edd.: καὶ τικτούς ceteri 12 καύσει Turnebus (in versione), Hill: θραύσει codd. ἄχρις ἂν Turnebus: * ἂν E: χρειαν, χρείαν, χρεῖαν, &c. ceteri. ὀσμὴ E: ὡς μὴ ceteri. 13 ὃν δὲ] δὲ om. F Aldus. σπῖνον] σπίνον Caley & Richards, fortasse recte; vide Liddell & Scott⁹, s.v. τοῖς μετάλλοις] τοῖς ⟨αὐτοῖς⟩ μετάλλοις Wimmer. τούτοις, οὗτος ego (οὗτος Turnebus): τοιοῦτος codd.

II. 9. Burning causes some stones to melt and become fluid. Take, for instance, those found in mines. When silver and copper and iron become fluid, the stone from them becomes fluid at the same time, possibly owing to the moist character of its constituents or possibly indeed through the agency of the metals. Similarly *pyromachi* and millstones become fluid along with the material heaped upon them by those who burn it. Some people even assert outright that all stones melt with the exception of limestone, which is calcined and turns into lime. 10. But this appears to be entirely an exaggeration, because there are many stones that break and burst asunder more violently even than earthenware in their struggle to resist the action of fire. This is actually what is to be expected of stones that have lost their moisture, since whatever is capable of being melted must be humid and contain much moisture. 11. It is said that some stones that are exposed to the sun dry up so completely that they are useless unless they are wetted and moistened again, while others are in consequence softer and more friable. It is clear that both kinds of stone are deprived of their moisture by the sun, but that the compact stones happen to harden as they dry, while the porous stones or rather those of porous consistency are rendered friable and brittle. 12. Some of these friable stones, when they are burnt, glow like charcoal and last a long time, as for instance those found in the mine near Binae which are washed down by the river there. When these are covered with charcoal, they burn and continue to do so as long as anyone blows upon them. After this they die down and are kindled again, and thus retain their use for a considerable time. Their smell, however, is very strong and disagreeable. 13. The stone known as 'spinos', which used to exist in these mines, burns when it is placed in the sun if it has been previously split up and arranged in a heap; and it burns all the more fiercely when water has been sprayed and sprinkled on and around it. 14. The Lipara stone, which before burning is black, smooth and dense, is not rendered porous by combustion, but also assumes the appearance of pumice, so that its colour changes along with its density. This stone does not occur as a continuous mass, but is found in separate 'cups' here and there amid the pumice, just as in Melos the pumice is said to be found within another stone. Thus

περιρράνῃ] περιράνῃ codd., edd.   14 ἐκπορούται ego: ἐκπωρούται coni. Salmasius: ἐκφορούται codd.   τε om. E.   δ' οὗτος] δὲ οὗτος Schneider, &c.   χυτριδίῳ (pro quo in archetypo scriptum esse videtur κυθριδίῳ) ego: κυθρισμῷ ADFGKLMN: κυθρισμῷ C: κυθερισμῷ E: κυττάρῳ Schneider, &c.: κυτταρείῳ Furlanus.   εἴη ἂν ego: εἰ μὲν FK²: lacunam post εἰ E: εἰ μαν ceteri codd.: ἐκεῖνος μὲν Furlanus.   τούτῳ] τοῦτο K².

62 THEOPHRASTUS

15 ἀντιπεπονθώς· πλὴν ὁ λίθος οὗτος οὐχ ὅμοιος τῷ Λιπαραίῳ. ἐκπορούται δὲ καὶ ὁ ἐν Τετράδι τῆς Σικελίας γινόμενος· τοῦτο δὲ τὸ χωρίον
ἐστὶ κατὰ Λιπάραν. ὁ δὲ λίθος ⟨ὁ⟩ ἐν τῇ ἄκρᾳ τῇ Ἐρινεάδι καλουμένῃ
πολὺς ὁμοίως τοῖς ἐν Βίναις καιόμενος ὀσμὴν ἀφίησιν ἀσφάλτου, τὸ δ'
16 ἐκ τῆς κατακαύσεως ὅμοιον γίνεται γῇ κεκαυμένῃ. οὓς δὲ καλοῦσιν
εὐθὺς ἄνθρακας τῶν ὀρυττομένων διὰ τὴν χρείαν εἰσὶ γεώδεις, ἐκ-
καίονται δὲ καὶ πυροῦνται καθάπερ οἱ ἄνθρακες. εἰσὶ δὲ περί τε τὴν
Λιγυστικὴν ὅπου καὶ τὸ ἤλεκτρον, καὶ ἐν τῇ Ἠλείᾳ βαδιζόντων
17 Ὀλυμπίαζε τὴν δι' ὄρους, οἷς καὶ οἱ χαλκεῖς χρῶνται. εὑρέθη δέ
ποτε ἐν τοῖς ἐν Σκαπτῇ Ὕλῃ μετάλλοις λίθος ὃς τῇ μὲν ὄψει παρ-
όμοιος ἦν ξύλῳ σαπρῷ, ὅτε δ' ἐπιχέοι τις τὸ ἔλαιον ἐκαίετο, καὶ ὅτ'
ἐκκαυθείη τότ' ἐπαύετο καὶ αὐτὸς ὥσπερ ἀπαθὴς ὤν. τῶν μὲν οὖν
καιομένων σχεδὸν αὗται διαφοραί.

18 III. Ἄλλο δέ τι γένος ἐστὶ λίθων ὥσπερ ἐξ ἐναντίων πεφυκός, ἄκαυστον
ὅλως, ἄνθραξ καλούμενος, ἐξ οὗ καὶ τὰ σφραγίδια γλύφουσιν, ἐρυθρὸν
μὲν τῷ χρώματι, πρὸς δὲ τὸν ἥλιον τιθέμενον ἄνθρακος καιομένου
ποιεῖ χρόαν. τιμιώτατον δ' ὡς εἰπεῖν· μικρὸν γὰρ σφόδρα τετταρά-
19 κοντα χρυσῶν. ἄγεται δὲ οὗτος ἐκ Καρχηδόνος καὶ Μασσαλίας. οὐ
καίεται δὲ ὁ περὶ Μίλητον γωνιοειδὴς ὢν ἐν ᾧπερ καὶ τὰ ἐξάγωνα.
καλοῦσι δ' ἄνθρακα καὶ τοῦτον. ὃ καὶ θαυμαστόν ἐστιν,—ὅμοιον γὰρ
τρόπον τινὰ καὶ τὸ τοῦ ἀδάμαντος,—οὐ γὰρ οὐδ' ὥσπερ ἡ κίσσηρις καὶ
τέφρα δόξειεν ἂν διὰ τὸ μηδὲν ἔχειν ὑγρόν· ταῦτα γὰρ ἄκαυστα καὶ
ἀπύρωτα διὰ τὸ ἐξηρῆσθαι τὸ ὑγρόν· ἐπεὶ καὶ τὸ ὅλον ἡ κίσσηρις ἐκ
κατακαύσεως δοκεῖ τισι γίνεσθαι, πλὴν τῆς ἐκ τοῦ ἀφροῦ τῆς θαλάσ-
20 σης συνισταμένης. λαμβάνουσι δὲ τὴν πίστιν διὰ τῆς αἰσθήσεως ἔκ τε
τῶν περὶ τοὺς κρατῆρας γενομένων καὶ ἐκ τῆς διαβόρου λίθου τῆς
φλογουμένης, ἣ κισσηροῦται. μαρτυρεῖν δὲ καὶ οἱ τόποι δοκοῦσιν ἐν

14 Λιπαραίῳ FK²M : λιπαρῷ ceteri. 15 ἐκπορούται; vide § 14. Τετράδι FKLM :
τεταρίδι ceteri. τῆς Σικελίας] τῆς om. M. τοῦτο δὲ om. H. Λιπάραν AN Turnebus : λιπάρας ceteri. ⟨ὁ⟩ ἐν ego. τοῖς ἐν Βίναις Turnebus ; cf. § 12, οἱ περὶ Βίνας :
ταῖς κίναις codd. : τῷ ἐν Βίναις Schneider. κατακαύσεως Turnebus : κατακλίσεως codd. :
γῇ Turnebus : τῇ codd. 16 ὀρυττομένων Turnebus (in versione), Wimmer : θριτο-
μένων F Aldus : θρυττομένων ceteri : θρυπτομένων Turnebus (in textu). χρείαν FKLM :
χρόαν ceteri. Λιγυστικὴν Furlanus : λυγιστικὴν codd. Ἠλείᾳ Furlanus : ἰλία codd.
17 ἐν τοῖς ἐν Σκαπτῇ Ὕλῃ ego : ἐν Σκαπτηούλης ὕλης codd. (lacunam ante ἐγκαπτῆς
ACEFGKLM) : ἐν Σκαπτηούλης aut ἐν τοῖς Σκαπτησούλης edd. ἦν ego : ὢν codd.
ἐπιχέοι τις τὸ ego : ἐπιχέοιτό τις codd. ἐκαίετο coni. Caley & Richards : ἐκκαίεται
codd. τότ' ἐπαύετο coni. Caley & Richards : τότε παύεται codd. ἀπαθὴς ὢν Furlanus :
ἀπαθὴς ἦν codd. 18 ὅλως] ὡς ὁ Turnebus. καλούμενος] καλούμενον Ε. σφόδρα]
σφοδρὸν F Aldus. 19 δὲ ὁ FM ; om. E : δύο ceteri. γωνιοειδὴς] γωνιώδης F
Aldus. καὶ τοῦτον. ὃ καὶ θαυμαστόν ἐστιν, ὅμοιον γὰρ, κτλ. sic distinxi (ἔστιν om.
M). ὅμοιον γὰρ] ὅμοιον καὶ F Aldus. κίσσηρις Schneider : κίττηρις FKLM : κίτηρις

there exists, so to speak, an inverse relationship between the Lipara stone and this Melian stone, except that the Melian stone is dissimilar to that of Lipara. 15. The stone found in Sicily at Tetras, which is opposite Lipara, is also rendered porous, while the stone which is burnt in large quantities on Cape Erineas in the same manner as that of Binae gives off the odour of asphalt, and the residue left by its combustion is like calcined earth. 16. Those stones which on account of their use are dug under the simple title of 'anthrakes' are earthy, but are ignited and burnt like charcoal. They are found in Liguria, where amber also exists, and in the territory of Elis on the mountain track leading to Olympia, and are used by smiths. 17. A stone which was found in the mines of Scaptehyle was similar in appearance to rotten wood, and would burn if olive oil was poured on it. When the oil had burnt away, the stone itself also would stop burning just as though it were unaffected by fire. These, then, are substantially the characteristic differences of stones that are burnt.

III. 18. There is another kind of stone known as 'anthrax' which is quite incombustible, just as though it were formed of matter contrary in nature. Signets are carved of it. It is of a red hue and when placed towards the sun produces the colour of live charcoal. This stone, which is imported from Carthage and Massilia, is virtually the most valuable, an extremely small specimen fetching forty gold staters. 19. Again, the stone from the neighbourhood of Miletus, which is angular and contains hexagons, does not burn. This too is called 'anthrax'. What is also surprising (and incidentally the properties of the *adamas* are in a manner similar) is that it does not seem in any way to be the absence of moisture that makes the *anthrax* incombustible, as is the case with pumice and cinders. These indeed are unaffected by fire and are incombustible precisely because their moisture has been removed. For pumice in general is held by some to be produced through a process of combustion, except for the kind that is formed of seafoam. 20. Their belief is derived from their observation of the pumice found near volcanic craters and also of the 'corroded' stone, which gives off flames and becomes just like pumice. The regions in which the formation of pumice occurs do in fact seem to support this conclusion, since it is mostly in those which are volcanic

ceteri.   δόξειεν *Turnebus*: δόξειε δ' *codd.*   ἐξηρῆσθαι] ἐξηρεῖσθαι FKL *Aldus.*   ἐπεί]
ἐπὶ N.   20 γενομένων *codd.*: γινομένων *Schneider.*   διαβόρου *Liddell & Scott*[9] (*s.v.*
διάβαρος) : διαβάρου *codd.*   ἦ κισσηροῦται EK *Turnebus, Caley & Richards*: οὐ κισσηροῦται F *Aldus, Wimmer*: ἦ κισσηροῦται M : ἦ κ. *ceteri*: ἦ καὶ κ. *Furlanus, Schneider.*

οἷς ἡ γένεσις· καὶ γὰρ ἐν τοῖς ⟨καιομένοις⟩ μάλιστα καὶ ἡ κίσσηρις.
21 τάχα δὲ ἡ μὲν οὕτως αἱ δ' ἄλλως καὶ πλείους τρόποι τῆς γενέσεως. ἡ
γὰρ ἐν Νισύρῳ καθάπερ ἐξ ἄμμου τινὸς ἔοικε συγκεῖσθαι.
σημεῖον δὲ
λαμβάνουσιν ὅτι τῶν εὑρισκομένων ἔνιαι διαθρύπτονται ἐν ταῖς χερσὶν
ὥσπερ εἰς ἄμμον διὰ τὸ μήπω συνεστάναι μηδὲ συμπεπηγέναι. εὑρίσκουσι δ' ἀθρόας κατὰ μικρὰ πολλὰς ὅσον χειροπληθεῖς ἢ μικρῷ
μείζους ὅταν ἀπαμήσωνται τἄνω· ἐλαφρὰ δὲ σφόδρα καὶ ἡ ἄμμος. ἡ
δ' αὖ ἐν Μήλῳ πᾶσα μὲν ⟨βαρεῖα⟩ ἔνια δ' αὖ ἐν λίθῳ τινὶ ἑτέρῳ
22 γίνεται καθάπερ ἐλέχθη πρότερον. διαφορὰς δ' ἔχουσι πρὸς ἀλλήλας
καὶ χρώματι καὶ πυκνότητι καὶ βάρει· χρώματι μὲν ὅτι μέλαινα ⟨ἡ⟩ ἐκ
τοῦ ῥύακος τοῦ ἐν Σικελίᾳ· πυκνότητι δὲ καὶ βάρει αὕτη γε καὶ
μυλώδης. γίνεται γάρ τις καὶ τοιαύτη κίσσηρις καὶ βάρος ἔχει καὶ
πυκνότητα καὶ ἐν τῇ χρήσει πολυτιμοτέρα τῆς ἑτέρας. σμηκτικὴ δὲ
καὶ ἡ ἐκ τοῦ ῥύακος μᾶλλον τῆς κούφης καὶ λευκῆς, σμηκτικωτάτη
δ' ⟨ἡ⟩ ἐκ τῆς θαλάσσης αὐτῆς. καὶ περὶ μὲν τῆς κισσήριδος ἐπὶ
τοσοῦτον εἰρήσθω. περὶ δὲ τῶν πυρουμένων καὶ τῶν ἀπυρώτων λίθων
ἀφ' ὧν καὶ εἰς τοῦτο ἐξέβημεν ἐν ἄλλοις θεωρητέον τὰς αἰτίας.

23 IV. Τῶν δὲ λίθων καὶ ἄλλαι ⟨περιτταὶ⟩ τυγχάνουσιν ἐξ ὧν καὶ τὰ
σφραγίδια γλύφουσιν, αἱ μὲν τῇ ὄψει μόνον οἷον τὸ σάρδιον καὶ ἡ
ἴασπις καὶ ἡ σάπφειρος· αὕτη δ' ἐστὶν ὥσπερ χρυσόπαστος. ἡ δὲ
σμάραγδος καὶ δυνάμεις τινὰς ἔχει· τοῦ τε γὰρ ὕδατος ὥσπερ εἴπομεν
ἐξομοιοῦται τὴν χρόαν ἑαυτῇ, μετρία μὲν οὖσα ἐλάττονος, ἡ δὲ μεγίστη
24 παντός, ἡ δὲ χειρίστη τοῦ καθ' αὑτὴν μόνον. καὶ πρὸς τὰ ὄμματα
ἀγαθή, διὸ καὶ τὰ σφραγίδια φοροῦσιν ἐξ αὐτῆς ὥστε βλέπειν· ἔστι δὲ
σπανία καὶ τὸ μέγεθος οὐ μεγάλη, πλὴν εἰ πιστεύειν ταῖς ἀναγραφαῖς
δεῖ ὑπὲρ τῶν βασιλέων τῶν Αἰγυπτίων· ἐκείνοις γάρ φασι κομι-
σθῆναί ποτ' ἐν δώροις παρὰ τοῦ Βαβυλωνίων βασιλέως μῆκος μὲν

20 ἐν τοῖς καιομένοις Schneider: ἐν ταῖς codd.: lacunam post ἐν τοῖς Wimmer, Caley
& Richards. 21 πολλὰς ὅσον χειροπληθεῖς coni. Schneider: χειροπληθεῖς ὅσον
πολλὰς Turnebus: χειροπληστίας ὅ. π. CEF Aldus: χειροπλιστίας ὅ. π. ceteri.
ἀπαμήσωνται Schneider: ἀπαμείβωνται codd.: ἀπαμῶνται Turnebus: ἀπαμείρωνται
Furlanus. καὶ ἡ ἄμμος] καὶ om. Schneider, Wimmer, Caley & Richards. αὖ
ACDEGN: αὖ καὶ FKLM edd. πᾶσα μὲν ⟨βαρεῖα⟩ ego: lacunam post πᾶσα μὲν codd.
ἑτέρῳ] ἑτέρᾳ F(?) Aldus. 22 ⟨ἡ⟩ ἐκ Caley & Richards e coni. Stephanidis.
πυκνότητι δὲ Schneider: πυκνότητί τε codd. (πυκνότητε N). αὕτη γε καὶ ego:
αὕτη τε καὶ Schneider, &c.: αὐτή τε καὶ codd. μυλώδης Furlanus: μαλώδης
codd.: ⟨ἡ⟩ μαλώδης Caley & Richards: ἀλμώδης Turnebus. πολυτιμοτέρα ACEGN
Caley & Richards: πολυτιμότερον FKLM: πολυτιμότερος BDHJ. σμηκτικὴ
Turnebus (in versione), Hill: τμητικὴ codd., Wimmer, Caley & Richards. ἡ ἐκ]
ἡ om. BH. ῥύακος μᾶλλον Turnebus: ῥικὸς (ῥινὸς CE) μᾶλλον codd. κούφης
Furlanus: κορυφῆς codd. σμηκτικωτάτη: vide supra σμηκτικὴ. δ' ⟨ἡ⟩ ἐκ
Caley & Richards e coni. Stephanidis. αὐτῆς ABCDEGHJN: αὐτοῦ FKLM.

that pumice exists. 21. But it is possible that, while some pumice is formed under such conditions, some is formed differently, and that there are several ways in which it is generated. For instance, the pumice of Nisyros appears to consist of a kind of sand. Evidence for this is derived from the fact that, when they are handled, some of the pumice-stones found there crumble into a kind of sand because they are not yet completely formed and solidified. Numerous pumice-stones are found clustered together in small pieces when the top soil is scraped away, the stones being approximately large enough to fill the hand or a little larger. Even the sand is of extremely light weight. On the other hand, all the pumice of Melos is heavy (?), and some of it is found within another stone, as was said before. 22. Pumices differ from each other in colour, solidity, and weight. They differ in colour inasmuch as the pumice from the Sicilian lava-flow is black, while in solidity and weight it is quite like a millstone. For pumice of this kind does indeed exist, weighty and solid and more valuable in use than the other kind. This pumice from the lava-flow is a better abrasive than the kind which is light in weight and white in colour, although that which comes actually from the sea is the best abrasive of all. So much for pumice. As for the stones from which we digressed to this subject, namely the stones that are affected and unaffected by fire, the causes of their behaviour must be considered elsewhere.

IV. 23. Other stones, of which signets are carved, are also found to be unusual. Some of these, the 'sard' and the *iaspis* for example and the *sapphirus*, which is speckled as if with gold, are unusual only in their appearance. The *smaragdus*, on the other hand, possesses also certain powers. For, as we have mentioned, it imparts its colour to water, the largest size affecting the whole volume of water, an average stone a smaller volume, and the poorest kind only the water adjacent to it. 24. Moreover, it is good for the eyes, and signets carved of it are worn to be looked at. It is, however, rare and of no great size, unless we are to trust the records relating to the kings of Egypt, according to which there was once brought to them, among other gifts from the king of

τῆς κισσήριδος] τῆς om. *Wimmer.*   23 ἄλλαι ⟨περιτταὶ⟩ *ego* : ἄλλαι ⟨διάφοροι⟩ *Wimmer, Caley & Richards* : lacunam post ἄλλαι codd.   ἡ ἴασπις FKM (ἡ om. M) : ἡ ἄσπις ceteri.   μὲν] μὲν οὖν BDHJ.   παντός *Turnebus* : πάντων E : πάντως ceteri.   24 σφραγίδια φοροῦσιν F edd. : σφραγίδια διαφοροῦσιν codd.   ἐκείνοις *Turnebus* (in versione), *Wimmer, Caley & Richards* : σμαράγδους B²H : lacunam ante νους ceteri codd. : ἔνιοι *Furlanus, Schneider.*   κομισθῆναι EF : κομησθῆναι K²LM : κοσμηθῆναι ACDGK¹N.

τετράπηχυν πλάτος δὲ τρίπηχυν. ἀνακεῖσθαι δὲ καὶ ἐν τῷ τοῦ Διὸς
ὀβελίσκους σμαράγδου τέτταρας, μῆκος μὲν τετταράκοντα πηχῶν,
εὖρος δὲ τῇ μὲν τέτταρας τῇ δὲ δύο. ταῦτα μὲν οὖν τὰ κατὰ τὴν
25 ἐκείνων γραφήν. τῶν δὲ Λακαινῶν καλουμένων ὑπὸ πολλῶν ἡ ἐν
Τύρῳ μεγίστη. στήλη γάρ ἐστιν εὐμεγέθης ἐν τῷ τοῦ Ἡρακλέους
ἱερῷ· εἰ μὴ ἄρα ψευδὴς σμάραγδος, καὶ γὰρ τοιαύτη γίνεταί τις φύσις.
γίνεται δὲ ἐν τοῖς ἐν ἐφικτῷ καὶ γνωρίμοις τόποις διτταχοῦ μάλιστα
περί τε Κύπρον ἐν τοῖς χαλκωρυχείοις καὶ ἐν τῇ νήσῳ τῇ ἐπικειμένῃ
Χαλκηδόνι. καὶ ἰδιωτέρως εὑρίσκουσιν ἐν ταύτῃ· μεταλλεύεται γὰρ
ὥσπερ τἆλλα καὶ ἡ φύσις, κατὰ ῥάβδους τείνουσα ἐν Κύπρῳ αὐτὴ καθ᾽
26 αὐτὴν πολλάς. εὑρίσκονται δὲ σπάνιαι μέγεθος ἔχουσαι σφραγῖδος
ἀλλ᾽ ἐλάττους αἱ πολλαί, διὸ καὶ πρὸς τὴν κόλλησιν αὐτῇ χρῶνται τοῦ
χρυσίου· κολλᾷ γὰρ ὥσπερ ἡ χρυσοκόλλα. καὶ ἔνιοί γε δὴ καὶ ὑπολαμ-
βάνουσι τὴν αὐτὴν φύσιν εἶναι· καὶ γὰρ τὴν χρόαν παρόμοιαι τυγχάνουσιν. ἀλλ᾽ ἡ μὲν χρυσοκόλλα δαψιλὴς καὶ ἐν τοῖς χρυσείοις καὶ
ἔτι μᾶλλον ἐν τοῖς χαλκωρυχείοις ὥσπερ ἐν τοῖς περὶ ⟨τούτους⟩ τοὺς
27 τόπους. ἡ δὲ σμάραγδος σπανία καθάπερ εἴρηται· δοκεῖ γὰρ ἐκ τῆς
ἰάσπιδος γίνεσθαι. φασὶ γὰρ εὑρεθῆναί ποτε ἐν Κύπρῳ λίθον ἧς τὸ
μὲν ἥμισυ σμάραγδος ἦν τὸ ἥμισυ δὲ ἴασπις ὡς οὔπω μεταβεβληκυίας
ἀπὸ τοῦ ὕδατος. ἔστι δέ τις αὐτῆς ἐργασία πρὸς τὸ λαμπρόν· ἀργὴ
γὰρ οὖσα οὐ λαμπρά.

28 V. Αὕτη τε δὴ περιττὴ τῇ δυνάμει καὶ τὸ λυγγούριον· καὶ γὰρ ἐκ
τούτου γλύφεται τὰ σφραγίδια καὶ ἔστι στερεωτάτη καθάπερ λίθος·
ἕλκει γὰρ ὥσπερ τὸ ἤλεκτρον, οἱ δέ φασιν οὐ μόνον κάρφη καὶ φύλλα
ἀλλὰ καὶ χαλκὸν καὶ σίδηρον ἐὰν ᾖ λεπτός, ὥσπερ καὶ Διοκλῆς ἔλεγεν.
ἔστι δὲ διαφανῆ τε σφόδρα καὶ ψυχρά. βελτίω δὲ τὰ τῶν ἀγρίων ἢ τὰ
τῶν ἡμέρων καὶ τὰ τῶν ἀρρένων ἢ τὰ τῶν θηλειῶν ὡς καὶ τῆς τροφῆς

24 ἀνακεῖσθαι . . . πηχῶν om. E.   ὀβελίσκους σμαράγδου τέτταρας Schneider e coni.
Salmasii : ὀβελίσκους σμαράγδους τέτταρας ACDGKLMN : ὀβελίσκῳ σμαράγδους τέτταρας F Aldus, Wimmer, Caley & Richards: ὀβέλισκον ἐκ σμαράγδων τεττάρων Turnebus
(in versione), de Laet.   μὲν οὖν τὰ ego : μὲν οὖν ὅτι codd., fortasse propter falsam tachy-
grammatis interpretationem (οὖν om. N).   γραφήν] ἀναγραφήν N.   25 Λακαινῶν ego : Βακτριανῶν Furlanus, Wimmer : τανῶν Turnebus (cum obelisco Caley & Richards) :
lacunam ante ανῶν codd.   καλουμένων Turnebus : καιομένων codd.   Τύρῳ] πύρῳ L.
διτταχοῦ]*χοῦ E.   μάλιστα] μάλιστα δὲ E.   χαλκωρυχείοις Turnebus: χαλκορυχείοις
codd., ceteri edd.   Χαλκηδόνι coni. Salmasius : Καρχηδόνι codd.   ἰδιωτέρως E Turnebus:
ἰδιωτέροις BH : ἰδιωτέρους ceteri et edd.   φύσις, κατὰ sic distinxi : φύσις. κατὰ codd.
(om. E).   τείνουσα ego : ποιοῦσιν codd.: ἐποίησεν Wimmer, Caley & Richards (coni.
Schneider).   αὐτὴ N : αὐτὴν ceteri codd., edd.   26 καὶ ἔνιοι . . . χρυσοκόλλα om. M.
παρόμοιαι EK : παρόμοια ceteri.   χρυσείοις F edd.: χρυσίοις ceteri.   ἐν τοῖς περὶ
⟨τούτους⟩ τοὺς τόπους ego : lacunam ante τοὺς Wimmer, Caley & Richards : ἐν τοῖς
τόποις BH: ἐν τοῖς περὶ τοὺς Στόβους Turnebus, Schneider.   27 Κύπρῳ EFKLM :

Babylon, a *smaragdus* which was four cubits long and three cubits broad. It is also stated that at the temple of Zeus there stand four obelisks of *smaragdus*, forty cubits in height with a breadth of four cubits at one extremity and two at the other. These, then, are the facts according to the records of the kings of Egypt. 25. As for the stones known to many as Laconian *smaragdi*, the largest is the one at Tyre, where a great block stands in the temple of Heracles, unless indeed this is a false *smaragdus*, of which a kind also exists.

There are two accessible and well-known places where the *smaragdus* is especially to be found, namely the copper mines of Cyprus and those of the island opposite Chalcedon. It is in this island that it comes to light in the more remarkable way. For here this kind of stone, which in Cyprus extends independently in numerous veins, is mined under the same conditions as the rest of the minerals. 26. But only a few of the stones found attain the size of a signet. The majority are smaller and are consequently used for soldering gold, which the *smaragdus* solders as effectively as does chrysocolla. Some people, indeed, assume that the two are identical in nature. Incidentally, they are identical in colour, but chrysocolla is abundant in gold-mines and still more so in copper-mines, as in those of these regions, (27) whereas the *smaragdus*, as has been said, is rare; and this is because it is apparently formed from the *iaspis*. It is stated that in Cyprus a stone was once found one half of which was a *smaragdus* and the other half an *iaspis*, as though the transformation of the stone from water were not yet complete. There is a method of working the *smaragdus* so as to achieve brilliance. If it is unworked, it is dull.

V. 28. Like the *smaragdus*, the *lyngurium*, which is carved into signets and is as hard as any stone, has an unusual power. For it attracts other objects just as amber does, and some people claim that it acts not only on straws and leaves, but also on thin pieces of copper and iron, as Diocles maintained. The *lyngurium* is cold and very clear. A wild lynx produces better stones than a tame animal, and a male better ones than a female, there being

κύθρῳ ceteri. ἀργὴ Schneider: ἀρχὴ codd. 28 αὕτη Turnebus (in versione), de Laet: αὐτή codd. φύλλα coni. Wimmer: ξύλον codd. An εὔσματα? ἔστι δὲ Schneider: ἔτι F Aldus: ἔτι δὲ ceteri codd. διαφανῆ codd.: διαφανές Schneider, &c. σφόδρα καὶ] καὶ σφόδρα καὶ C¹E¹. ψυχρά codd.: ψυχρόν Schneider, &c.: πυρρά Furlanus. βελτίω de Laet: βέλτιον codd. τὰ τῶν (quater) codd.: τὸ τῶν Schneider, &c.

διαφερούσης, καὶ τοῦ πονεῖν ἢ μὴ πονεῖν, καὶ τῆς τοῦ σώματος ὅλως
φύσεως, ᾗ ξηρότερον τὸ δ᾽ ὑγρότερον. εὑρίσκουσι δ᾽ ἀνορύττοντες οἱ
ἔμπειροι· κατακρύπτεται γὰρ καὶ ἐπαμᾶται γῆν ὅταν οὐρήσῃ. γίνεται
29 δὲ καὶ κατεργασία τις αὐτοῦ πλείων. ἐπεὶ δὲ καὶ τὸ ἤλεκτρον λίθος,
καὶ γὰρ ὀρυκτὸν τὸ περὶ ⟨τὴν⟩ Λιγυστικήν, καὶ τούτῳ ἂν ἡ τοῦ ἕλκειν
δύναμις ἀκολουθοίη. μάλιστα δὲ δηλονότι ⟨ἕλκει⟩ καὶ φανερώταθ᾽
ἡ τὸν σίδηρον ἄγουσα. γίνεται δὲ καὶ αὕτη σπανία καὶ ὀλιγαχοῦ. καὶ
30 αὕτη μὲν δὴ συναριθμείσθω τὴν δύναμιν ὁμοίαν ἔχειν. ἐξ ὧν δὲ τὰ
σφραγίδια ποιεῖται καὶ ἄλλαι πλείους εἰσίν, οἷον ἥ θ᾽ ὑαλοειδής, ἢ καὶ
ἔμφασιν ποιεῖ καὶ διάφασιν, καὶ τὸ ἀνθράκιον, καὶ ἡ ὄμφαξ· ἔτι δὲ
καὶ ἡ κρύσταλλος καὶ τὸ ἀμέθυσον, ἄμφω δὲ διαφανῆ, εὑρίσκονται δὲ
καὶ αὗται καὶ τὸ σάρδιον διακοπτομένων τινῶν πετρῶν. καὶ ἄλλαι δὲ ὡς
προείρηται πρότερον διαφορὰς ἔχουσαι καὶ συνώνυμοι πρὸς ἀλλήλας.
τοῦ γὰρ σαρδίου τὸ μὲν διαφανὲς ἐρυθρότερον δὲ καλεῖται θῆλυ, τὸ δὲ
31 διαφανὲς μὲν μελάντερον δὲ ἄρρεν. καὶ τὰ λυγγούρια δὲ ὡσαύτως, ὧν
τὸ θῆλυ διαφανέστερον καὶ ξανθότερον. καλεῖται δὲ καὶ κύανος ὁ μὲν
ἄρρην ὁ δὲ θῆλυς· μελάντερος δὲ ὁ ἄρρην. τὸ δ᾽ ὀνύχιον μικτὸν λευκῷ
καὶ φαιῷ παρ᾽ ἄλληλα. τὸ δ᾽ ἀμέθυσον οἰνωπὸν τῇ χρόᾳ. καλὸς δὲ
λίθος καὶ ὁ ἀχάτης ὁ ἀπὸ τοῦ Ἀχάτου ποταμοῦ τοῦ ἐν Σικελίᾳ καὶ
32 πωλεῖται τίμιος. ἐν Λαμψάκῳ δέ ποτ᾽ ἐν τοῖς χρυσείοις εὑρέθη
θαυμαστὴ λίθος ἐξ ἧς ἀνενεχθείσης πρὸς Ἄστυρα (?) σφραγίδιον γλυφθὲν ἀνεπέμφθη βασιλεῖ διὰ τὸ περιττόν.

33 VI. Καὶ αὗται μὲν ἅμα τῷ καλῷ καὶ τὸ σπάνιον ἔχουσιν. αἱ δὲ δὴ ἐκ
τῆς Ἑλλάδος εὐτελέστεραι, οἷον τὸ ἀνθράκιον τὸ ἐξ Ὀρχομενοῦ τῆς
Ἀρκαδίας. ἔστι δὲ οὗτος μελάντερος τοῦ Χίου· κάτοπτρα δὲ ἐξ αὐτοῦ
ποιοῦσι· καὶ ὁ Τροιζήνιος· οὗτος δὲ ποικίλος τὰ μὲν φοινικοῖς τὰ δὲ
λευκοῖς χρώμασι. ποικίλος δὲ καὶ ὁ Κορίνθιος τοῖς αὐτοῖς χρώμασι
34 πλὴν τὸ λευκὸν χλωροειδέστερον. τὸ δ᾽ ὅλον πολλοὶ τυγχάνουσιν οἱ

28 καὶ τῆς τοῦ σώματος ὅλως φύσεως om. FKLM Aldus, Turnebus, Schneider (in textu).
ᾗ ξηρότερον om. FKLM Aldus, Turnebus, Schneider (in textu): ᾗ τὸ μὲν ξηρότερον
Furlanus, Wimmer, Caley & Richards: εἰ ξηρότερον E. ἔμπειροι] ἔμπυροι A: ἔμποροι
E. οὐρήσῃ Turnebus: εὑρήσῃ CEF: εὑρήσει ceteri. 29 ἐπεὶ δὲ] ἔπειτα Schneider.
καὶ γὰρ ... τὸ περὶ Furlanus: τὸ γὰρ ... ὃ περὶ codd., Schneider, &c. ⟨τὴν⟩ supplevi;
cf. § 16. Λιγυστικήν coni. Salmasius: λυγγιστήν codd. τούτῳ FGKLM: τούτων
ceteri. ἀκολουθοίη A: ἀκολουθείη ceteri. δὲ δηλονότι ego: δ᾽ ὅτι δῆλον codd.: δ᾽
ἐπίδηλος Wimmer. ⟨ἕλκει⟩ καὶ ego. φανερώταθ᾽ ἡ ego: φανερωτάτη codd.: φανερωτάτη ἡ Wimmer. ἄγουσα E Wimmer: ἄγουσι ceteri codd. 30 ἔμφασιν] ἔμφεισιν BH. καλεῖται FKLM: καὶ καλεῖται ceteri. μὲν μελάντερον] μελάντερον
μὲν N. ἄρρεν ego; cf. §§ 28, 31: καὶ ἄρσεν codd. (καὶ in uncis posuerunt Schneider,
&c.). 31 ἄρρην de Laet: ἄρρεν codd. θῆλυς de Laet: θῆλυ codd. δὲ ὁ ἄρρην A:
δὲ ὁ ἄρρεν (δ᾽ ὁ F) ceteri. μικτὸν Wimmer: μικτὴ codd. οἰνωπὸν] οἴνοππον B¹:
οἴνοπον B²HJ. Ἀχάτου EFKM: ὀχάτου ceteri. 32 χρυσείοις ego; cf. §§ 26, 51:
χρυσίοις codd. Ἄστυρα coni. Schneider: στιρρὰν CE: στιρὰν ceteri codd., Wimmer:

a difference in diet, in the exercise taken or not taken, and, in general, in the natural constitution of the body, inasmuch as the body is drier in the case of the former and more moist in the case of the latter. The stone is discovered only when experienced searchers dig it up, for when the lynx has passed its urine, it conceals it and scrapes soil over it. Moreover, the *lyngurium* needs considerable working. 29. Similarly amber is a stone (for the amber of Liguria is dug from the earth), and of this likewise a power of attraction is an attribute. However, the stone with the strongest and most conspicuous power of attraction is clearly that which draws iron, but this stone too is rare and is found only in a few places. It should of course be included in our list as possessing such a power. 30. There are many other stones, too, of which signets are made, such as the *hyaloides*, which reflects images as well as being transparent, the *anthrakion* and the *omphax*. Again, we have the rock-crystal and the amethyst, both of which are transparent and are found, like the 'sard', by splitting certain rocks. Then there are some which, as we mentioned before, differ from each other although they share the same name. For instance, there is the 'sard', of which the transparent, ruddier kind is known as the 'female', while the transparent but darker variety is known as the 'male'. 31. The same is true of the *lyngurium*, the 'female' being the more transparent and the paler. *Cyanus* also is termed 'male' and 'female', the 'male' variety being the darker. The onyx is a mixture of white and grey arranged in parallel layers, while the amethyst has the colour of red wine. A handsome stone which fetches a high price is the agate from the river Achates in Sicily. 32. In the gold-mines at Lampsacus a remarkable stone was once found. This was taken to Astyra (?), where a signet was carved from it and sent to the Persian king because it was so unusual.

VI. 33. These stones are rare as well as beautiful, but those of Greece are of course less valuable. We may take as examples the *anthrakion* of Orchomenos in Arcadia, which is darker than the Chian stone and is made into mirrors, and the stone of Troezen, which is variegated dark-red and white. The Corinthian stone is similarly variegated, except that the white has a yellow tinge. 34. In general, there are many stones of this kind to be met with,

Τίραν Turnebus: ἡμέραν Rossbach. γλυφθὲν Turnebus: γλυφερὸν codd. βασιλεῖ]
⟨Ἀλεξάνδρῳ⟩ βασιλεῖ Schneider, Wimmer (Ἀλεξάνδρῳ βασιλεῖ Turnebus). 33 ἐξ
Ὀρχομενοῦ Turnebus; cf. Plinium 37. 97: ἐξορχομενου B²H²: ἐξερχόμενον (δ'
ἐξερχόμενον K) ceteri. κάτοπτρα Turnebus; cf. Plinium 37. 97: κάθοπτρα B²: καθὸ
B¹DFJN: κάθοπτος καθὸ H: κα* E: καθοὶ ACGKLM. τὸ λευκὸν χλωροειδέστερον
B²H: λευκὸν om. cum lacuna ceteri codd. (τὸ om. E): ὅτι χλωροειδέστερος Schneider, &c.

τοιοῦτοι ἀλλ' οἱ περιττοὶ σπάνιοι καὶ ἐξ ὀλίγων τόπων, οἷον ἔκ τε
Καρχηδόνος καὶ ἐκ τῶν περὶ Μασσαλίαν καὶ ἐξ Αἰγύπτου κατὰ τοὺς
Καταδούπους καὶ Συήνην πρὸς Ἐλεφαντίνῃ πόλει καὶ ἐκ τῆς Ψεφὼ
35 καλουμένης χώρας. καὶ ἐν Κύπρῳ ἥ τε σμάραγδος καὶ ἡ ἴασπις. οἷς
δὲ εἰς τὰ λιθοκόλλητα χρῶνται ἐκ τῆς Βακτριανῆς εἰσι πρὸς τῇ ἐρήμῳ.
συλλέγουσι δὲ αὐτοὺς ὑπὸ τοὺς ἐτησίας ἱππεῖς ἐξιόντες· τότε γὰρ
ἐμφανεῖς γίνονται κινουμένης τῆς ἄμμου διὰ τὸ μέγεθος τῶν πνευ-
36 μάτων. εἰσὶ δὲ μικροὶ καὶ οὐ μεγάλοι. τῶν σπουδαζομένων δὲ λίθων
ἐστὶ καὶ ὁ μαργαρίτης καλούμενος, διαφανὴς μὲν τῇ φύσει, ποιοῦσι
δ' ἐξ αὐτοῦ τοὺς πολυτελεῖς ὅρμους. γίνεται δὲ ἐν ὀστρείῳ τινὶ
παραπλησίῳ ταῖς πίνναις ⟨πλὴν ἐλάττονι· μέγεθος δὲ ἡλίκον ἰχθύος
ὀφθαλμὸς εὐμεγέθης⟩, φέρει δ' ἥ τε Ἰνδικὴ χώρα καὶ νῆσοί τινες τῶν
37 ἐν τῇ Ἐρυθρᾷ. τὸ μὲν οὖν περιττὸν σχεδὸν ἐν ταύταις. εἰσὶ δὲ καὶ
ἄλλαι τινές, οἷον ὅ τε ἐλέφας ὁ ὀρυκτὸς ποικίλος μέλανι καὶ λευκῷ
καὶ ἣν καλοῦσι σάπφειρον· αὕτη γὰρ μέλαινα οὐκ ἄγαν πόρρω τοῦ
κυάνου τοῦ ἄρρενος. καὶ ⟨ἡ⟩ πρασῖτις· αὕτη δὲ ἰώδης τῇ χρόᾳ.
πυκνὴ δὲ καὶ ⟨ἡ⟩ αἱματῖτις· αὕτη δ' αὐχμώδης καὶ κατὰ τοὔνομα ὡς
αἵματος ξηροῦ πεπηγότος. ἄλλη δ' ἡ καλουμένη ξανθή, οὐ ξανθὴ μὲν
τὴν χρόαν, ἔκλευκος δὲ μᾶλλον, ὃ καλοῦσι χρῶμα οἱ Δωριεῖς ξανθόν.
38 τὸ γὰρ κουράλιον, καὶ γὰρ τοῦθ' ὥσπερ λίθος, τῇ χρόᾳ μὲν ἐρυθρόν,
περιφερὲς δ' ὡς ἂν ῥίζα· φύεται δ' ἐν τῇ θαλάττῃ. τρόπον δέ τιν' οὐ
πόρρω τούτου τῇ φύσει καὶ ὁ Ἰνδικὸς κάλαμος ἀπολελιθωμένος. ταῦτα
μὲν οὖν ἄλλης σκέψεως.

39 VII. Τῶν δὲ λίθων πολλαί τινες αἱ φύσεις καὶ τῶν μεταλλευομένων.
ἔνιαι γὰρ ἅμα χρυσὸν ἔχουσι καὶ ἄργυρον, προφανῆ δὲ μόνον ἄργυρον·
βαρύτεραι δὲ αὗται πολὺ καὶ τῇ ῥοπῇ καὶ τῇ ὀσμῇ· καὶ κύανος αὐτοφυὴς
ἔχων ἐν ἑαυτῷ χρυσοκόλλαν. ἄλλη δὲ λίθος ὁμοία τὴν χρόαν τοῖς
40 ἄνθραξι, βάρος δ' ἔχουσα. καὶ τῶν μὲν τοιούτων πλείους ἄν τις λάβοι
41 τὰς ἰδιότητας. ἔνιαι δὲ λίθοι καὶ τὰς τοιαύτας ἔχουσι δυνάμεις εἰς τὸ
μὴ πάσχειν, ὥσπερ εἴπομεν, οἷον τὸ μὴ γλύφεσθαι σιδηρίοις ἀλλὰ

34 Μασσαλίαν M : Μασαλίαν ceteri.   Καταδούπους Schneider : κατάδου τόπους codd.
Συήνην ego : Συήνης Turnebus : Συήνη codd.   Ψεφὼ codd. : Ψεβὼ coni. Salmasius.
35 λιθοκόλλητα Schneider : λιθόκολλα codd.   τῆς Βακτριανῆς] τῆς Βακτριανοῖς DJ : τοῖς
Βακτριανοῖς BH.   τοὺς ἐτησίας] τοὺς om. F Aldus : τοὺς ἐτησίους CᴵÌ.   κινουμένης
CEFK²M : κενουμένης ADGKᴵLN.   36 σπουδαζομένων codd. : θαυμαζομένων
Athenaeus.   διαφανὴς codd. : οὐ διαφανὴς Hill e coni. Salmasii.   τοὺς πολυτελεῖς : τοὺς
om. Wimmer.   παραπλησίῳ] παραπλησίως Hill.   πλὴν ἐλάττονι . . . εὐμεγέθης add.
Schneider, &c., ex Athenaeo iii, 93a–b; om. codd.   ἡλίκον Athenaeus : ἡλίκος Clemens
Alexandrinus, edd.   ταύταις Schneider : αὐταῖς codd.   37 ὅ τε] τε om. Schneider, &c.
ἐλέφας FM : ἀλάφορας Bᴵ : ἀλάφας ceteri.   ὀρυκτὸς K² : ὀρεκτὸς ceteri codd.   ποικίλος]
ποικίλοις L.   καὶ λευκῷ om. F Aldus, Turnebus.   ⟨ἡ⟩ πρασῖτις ego.   ⟨ἡ⟩ αἱματῖτις

but the remarkable ones are rare and come from only a few
places, from Carthage for example, from the districts near Mas-
salia, from Egypt around the Cataract and Syene near the city of
Elephantine, and from the region known as Psepho. 35. And in
Cyprus there is the *smaragdus* and the *iaspis*.

Those stones used in
inlay work come from the neighbourhood of the Bactrian Desert
and are collected by expeditions of men on horseback in the
season of the Etesians, when the high winds shift the sand and
expose them to view. The stones are small, or rather, not large.
36. The so-called 'pearl', which is transparent in nature and is
made into costly necklaces, also ranks as a precious stone. It
grows in an oyster which is comparable to the *pinna*, but smaller.
The dimensions of the pearl are those of a fish's eye of large size,
and it is produced off the coast of India and certain islands in the
Red Sea. These, then, are substantially the stones which possess
an unusual character. 37. There are also others, for example
fossil ivory, which has black and white markings, the stone known
as *sapphirus*, which is dark and does not differ greatly from the
'male' kind of *cyanus*, and the *prasitis*, which has the colour of
verdigris. A solid stone is the *haematitis*, which has a dull appearance and, as its name implies, looks like congealed blood.
Another stone is the so-called 'xanthe', which is not so much
yellow in colour as whitish, 'xanthos' being the term used for this
colour in the Dorian dialect. 38. Incidentally, the coral, which is
just like a stone, is red in colour and rounded like a root, and
grows in the sea. In some respects the Indian reed, when it has
turned to stone, is not so very different from coral in nature.
These, however, call for separate consideration.

VII. 39. There are also many kinds of stone extracted from mines.
Of these, some contain gold as well as silver, but only the silver
is clearly perceptible. Their weight is rather heavy and their
smell rather offensive. There is also a natural *cyanus* which contains chrysocolla, and another stone which is like charcoal in
colour, but heavy. 40. One could find quite a number of peculiarities belonging to such stones. 41. However, certain stones have
also powers of the kind mentioned earlier, in that they do not
react to extraneous forces: for example, they cannot be carved

ego. καὶ κατὰ *Turnebus (in versione), Schneider:* ἡ κατὰ *codd.* δ' ἡ καλουμένη ξανθή
K² *Turnebus (in versione), Schneider* (δὲ ἡ): δὴ καλουμένη (δῆ A, δὲ EJ) *codd.* δὲ
μᾶλλον ὃ *Turnebus (in versione), Schneider:* δ' ὃ μᾶλλον *codd.* Δωριεῖς E: δωρεῖς
ceteri. 38 ὡς ἂν] ἂν *om. Wimmer.* 39 ἔνιαι *Furlanus:* ἔνια *codd.:* ἔνιοι
Turnebus. δ' ἔχουσα *Schneider:* δ' ἔχουσι *codd.* (δὲ *Wimmer*). 40 τὸ ὅλον . . .
ὅμοια τούτοις *ex initio huius sectionis in* § 50 *transtuli; vide commentarium ad loc.*

λίθοις ἑτέροις. ὅλως μὲν ἡ κατὰ τὰς ἐργασίας καὶ τῶν μειζόνων λίθων
πολλὴ διαφορά. πριστοὶ γάρ, οἱ δὲ γλυπτοί, καθάπερ ἐλέχθη, καὶ
τορνευτοὶ τυγχάνουσι, καθάπερ καὶ ἡ μαγνῆτις αὕτη λίθος ἡ καὶ
⟨τῇ⟩ ὄψει ⟨τὸ⟩ περιττὸν ἔχουσα, καὶ ἧς γε δή τινες θαυμάζουσι τὴν
42 ὁμοίωσιν τῷ ἀργύρῳ μηδαμῶς οὔσης συγγενοῦς. πλείους δ' εἰσὶν οἱ
δεχόμενοι πάσας τὰς ἐργασίας. ἐπεὶ καὶ ἐν Σίφνῳ τοιοῦτός τίς ἐστιν
ὀρυκτὸς ὡς τρία στάδια ἀπὸ θαλάττης, στρογγύλος καὶ βωλώδης, καὶ
τορνεύεται καὶ γλύφεται διὰ τὸ μαλακόν· ὅταν δὲ πυρωθῇ καὶ ἀποβαφῇ τῷ ἐλαίῳ, μέλας τε σφόδρα γίνεται καὶ σκληρός. ποιοῦσι δ' ἐξ
43 αὐτοῦ σκεύη τὰ ἐπιτράπεζα. οἱ μὲν τοιοῦτοι πάντες προσδέχονται
τὴν τοῦ σιδήρου δύναμιν· ἔνιοι δὲ λίθοις ἄλλοις γλύφονται, σιδηρίοις δ'
οὐ δύνανται καθάπερ εἴπομεν. οἱ δὲ σιδηρίοις μὲν ἀμβλυτέροις δέ· καὶ
εἰσὶν ⟨ἄλλαι διαφοραί (?)⟩. παραπλησίως δὲ καὶ ἄτοπον τὸ ⟨ἐνίους⟩
μὴ τέμνεσθαι ⟨τῷ⟩ σιδήρῳ· καίτοι τὰ στερεώτερα ⟨ὅλως⟩ ἰσχυρότερον
44 τέμνει καὶ ⟨ὁ⟩ σίδηρος λίθου σκληρότερος ὤν. ἄτοπον δὲ κἀκεῖνο φαίνεται διότι ἡ μὲν ἀκόνη κατεσθίει τὸν σίδηρον, ὁ δὲ σίδηρος ταύτην μὲν
δύναται διαιρεῖν καὶ ῥυθμίζειν, ἐξ ἧς δ' αἱ σφραγῖδες οὔ. καὶ πάλιν
ὁ λίθος ᾧ γλύφουσι τὰς σφραγῖδας ἐκ τούτου ἐστὶν ἐξ οὗπερ αἱ ἀκόναι,
45 ἢ ἐξ ὁμοίου τούτῳ· ἄγεται δὲ ἡ ⟨βελτίστη⟩ ἐξ Ἀρμενίας. θαυμαστὴ δὲ
φύσις καὶ τῆς βασανιζούσης τὸν χρυσόν· δοκεῖ γὰρ δὴ τὴν αὐτὴν
ἔχειν τῷ πυρὶ δύναμιν· καὶ γὰρ ἐκεῖνο δοκιμάζει. διὸ καὶ ἀποροῦσί
τινες οὐκ ἄγαν οἰκείως ἀποροῦντες. οὐ γὰρ τὸν αὐτὸν τρόπον δοκιμάζει,
ἀλλὰ τὸ μὲν πῦρ τῷ τὰ χρώματα μεταβάλλειν καὶ ἀλλοιοῦν, ὁ δὲ λίθος
τῇ παρατρίψει· δύναται γὰρ ὡς ἔοικεν ἐκλαμβάνειν τὴν ἑκάστου φύσιν.
46 εὑρῆσθαι δέ φασι νῦν ἀμείνω πολὺ τῆς πρότερον ὥστε μὴ μόνον τὸν ἐκ
τῆς καθάρσεως ἀλλὰ καὶ τὸν κατάχαλκον χρυσὸν καὶ ἄργυρον γνωρίζειν

41 ⟨τῇ⟩ ὄψει ⟨τὸ⟩ περιττὸν Schneider. Cf. H.P. 9. 7. 2, τὰ περιττὰ τῇ ὀσμῇ.   ἧς
γε . . . οὔσης συγγενοῦς Wimmer (coni. Schneider): ὥς γε . . . οὔσαν συγγενῆ codd.
42 ὀρυκτὸς ὡς K Turnebus: ὀρεκτὸς ὡς codd.   βωλώδης Schneider: βόλασος codd.   ὅταν
δὲ] δὲ om. F Aldus.   καὶ ἀποβαφῇ om. F Aldus.   τῷ ἐλαίῳ] τῷ in uncis posuit Wimmer.
σφόδρα] σφοδρότερον CE.   43 οἱ μὲν] οἱ μὲν ⟨οὖν⟩ Schneider, &c.   προσδέχονται]
ὑποδέχονται Heinsius.   δύναμιν] τὸ μὲν (?) δύναμιν E.   σιδηρίοις δ' . . . σιδηρίοις
μὲν ego; cf. §§ 5, 41.   σιδηρίοις δ' . . . σιδηρίοις μὲν codd.   ἀμβλυτέροις δέ Turnebus;
cf. Plinium 37. 200: ἀμ* δὲ codd. (ἀμ* om. E): ἀμβλέσι δέ Furlanus.   καὶ εἰσὶν ⟨ἄλλαι
διαφοραί (?)⟩ ego: καὶ εἰσὶν* codd.   παραπλησίως δὲ καὶ ἄτοπον ego (ἄτοπον sub voce
κάτω latere coni. Wimmer, sed καὶ ἄτοπον latere veri similius est): παραπλησίως δὲ κάτω
codd. Post παρὰ codd. BH ad textum libri a Theophrasto de Sudore scripti transeunt.   τὸ
⟨ἐνίους⟩ μὴ τέμνεσθαι ego: τα* μὴ τέμνεσθαι codd.: τὸ ὅλως μὴ τέμνεσθαι λίθον coni.
Stephanides.   ⟨τῷ⟩ σιδήρῳ] ⟨τῷ⟩ supplevi: σιδήρῳ FKLM: *ρω ceteri codd. (ρω
om. E).   τὰ στερεώτερα ⟨ὅλως⟩ ἰσχυρότερον ego: καὶ στερεὸν ετε* ἰσχυρότερα codd.
(ετε om. E): καὶ στερεώτερα καὶ ἰσχυρότερα Turnebus.   καὶ ⟨ὁ⟩ σίδηρος] καὶ om.
Turnebus: ⟨ὁ⟩ supplevi.   λίθου Turnebus: λίθους codd.   44 ἐξ ἧς δ'] ἐξ ἧς δὲ M
Schneider.   ᾧ γλύφουσι Turnebus: τῷ γλύφουσι codd.   ἡ ⟨βελτίστη⟩ ego: ἢ M: ἡ om. E:
ἡ ⟨ἀρίστη⟩ Schneider; sed cf. §§ 52, 55.   45 τὴν αὐτὴν Turnebus (in versione),

by iron tools, but only by other stones. Generally speaking, even
the larger stones differ greatly in the methods of working that
they admit. For, as we stated earlier, some can be sawn, and
others carved or turned on a lathe, like this 'magnetis', which
indeed has an unusual appearance and is admired by some for
its likeness to silver, although it is in no way akin to it. 42. There
are fairly numerous stones, however, that admit of every method
of working. For example, a stone of this kind which is dug in the
island of Siphnos about three furlongs from the sea is round,
clod-like, and soft enough to be both turned on the lathe and
carved. But when it is dipped in oil and fired, it becomes extremely dark and hard. Tableware is made of it. 43. All stones of
this kind submit to the force of iron, but certain others, as we
have said, cannot be carved by iron tools, but only by other
stones. Some again may be carved by iron tools, but only if they
are rather blunt. There are also other differences of this kind (?).
It is almost equally strange that some stones are not quarried by
iron (?). And yet in general the more recalcitrant substances are
cut more strongly by iron, which is harder than stone (?). 44. It is
also strange that, while whetstones erode iron, iron in its turn
should be able to split and shape whetstones and yet be power-
less similarly to affect stones of which signets are made. Moreover,
the whetstone and the stone by means of which signets are carved
are of similar, if not identical, material. The best whetstones come
from Armenia. 45. The character of the stone that tests gold is remarkable in that it appears to have the same power as fire, which
also tests gold. Consequently some people question the truth of
this, but their objections are not very relevant because the
methods of testing are different, involving a change and alteration of colour in the case of fire, and a comparison of marks made
by friction in the case of the stone, which seems to have the power
of abstracting the essential quality of each sample. 46. It is said
that a stone has now been discovered which is far superior to the
kind previously known, and detects the quality not only of re-
fined gold, but also of copper alloyed with gold or with silver

Schneider: τὴν τοιαύτην codd.   ἔχειν τῷ πυρὶ δύναμιν FKLM *edd.*: δ. ἔ. τ. π. *ceteri*.
ἐκεῖνο FK²LM: ἐκεῖ *ceteri*.   διὸ καὶ...δοκιμάζει *om.* E.   τῷ τὰ F *Aldus*: τὸ τὰ *ceteri*.
ἀλλοιοῦν E *Turnebus*: ἀξιοῦν (ἀξοιῦν F *Aldus*) *ceteri codd.*   46 φασι νῦν A: φασιν
νῦν *ceteri*.   τὸν κατάχαλκον χρυσὸν *Schneider*: τὸν χαλκὸν κατὰ χρυσὸν (καταχρυσὸν
C) *codd.*

καὶ πόσον εἰς τὸν στατῆρα μέμικται. σημεῖα δ᾽ ἐστὶν αὐτοῖς ἀπὸ τοῦ
ἐλαχίστου· ἐλάχιστον δὲ γίνεται [κριθή, εἶτα κόλλυβος, εἶτα] τεταρ-
47 τημόριον ἢ ἡμιωβόλιον, ἐξ ὧν γνωρίζουσι τὸ καθῆκον. εὑρίσκονται
δὲ τοιαῦται πᾶσαι ἐν τῷ ποταμῷ Τμώλῳ. λεία δ᾽ ἡ φύσις αὐτῶν καὶ
ψηφοειδής, πλατεῖα, οὐ στρογγύλη. μέγεθος δὲ ὅσον διπλασία τῆς
μεγίστης ψήφου. διαφέρει δ᾽ αὐτῆς πρὸς τὴν δοκιμασίαν τὰ ἄνω ⟨τὰ⟩
πρὸς τὸν ἥλιον ἢ τὰ κάτω καὶ βέλτιον δοκιμάζει τὰ ἄνω· τοῦτο δὲ ὅτι
ξηρότερα τὰ ἄνω· κωλύει γὰρ ἡ ὑγρότης εἰς τὸ ἐκλαμβάνειν· ἐπειδὴ
καὶ ἐν τοῖς καύμασι τὸ δοκιμάζειν χεῖρον· ἀνίησι γάρ τινα νοτίδα ἐξ
αὐτῆς δι᾽ ἣν ἀπολισθαίνει. συμβαίνει δὲ τοῦτο καὶ ἄλλοις τῶν λίθων,
καὶ ἐξ ὧν τὰ ἀγάλματα ποιοῦσιν, ὃ καὶ σημεῖον ὑπολαμβάνεται ὡς
ἰδίοντος τοῦ ἔδους.

48 **VIII.** Αἱ μὲν οὖν τῶν λίθων διαφοραὶ καὶ δυνάμεις σχεδόν εἰσιν ἐν
τούτοις. αἱ δὲ τῆς γῆς ἐλάττονες μὲν ἰδιώτεραι δέ. τὸ μὲν γὰρ τήκεσθαι
καὶ μαλάττεσθαι καὶ πάλιν ἀποσκληρύνεσθαι καὶ ταύτῃ συμβαίνει.
τήκεται μὲν γὰρ ⟨ἅμα⟩ τοῖς χυτοῖς καὶ ὀρυκτοῖς ὥσπερ καὶ ὁ λίθος·
μαλάττεται δέ, λίθους τε ποιοῦσιν, οἷον τάς τε ποικίλας καὶ τὰς ἄλλας
49 συντιθεμένας. ἁπάσας γὰρ πυροῦντες καὶ μαλάττοντες ποιοῦσιν. εἰ
δὲ καὶ ὁ ὕελος ἐκ τῆς ὑελίτιδος ὥς τινές φασι, καὶ αὕτη πυρώσει
γίνεται. ἰδιωτάτη δ᾽ ἡ τῷ χαλκῷ μιγνυμένη· πρὸς γὰρ τῷ τήκεσθαι
καὶ μίγνυσθαι καὶ δύναμιν ἔχει περιττὴν ὥστε τῷ κάλλει τῆς χρόας
ποιεῖν διαφοράν. περὶ δὲ Κιλικίαν ἐστί τις ἢ ἕψεται γῆ καὶ γίνεται
γλισχρά· ταύτῃ δ᾽ ἀλείφουσι τὰς ἀμπέλους ἀντὶ ἰξοῦ πρὸς τοὺς ἶπας.
50 εἴη δ᾽ ἂν λαμβάνειν καὶ ταύτας τὰς διαφορὰς ὅσαι πρὸς τὴν ἀπολίθωσιν
εὐφυεῖς· ἐπεὶ αἵ γε τοὺς τούτων ποιοῦσαι χυμοὺς διαφόρους ἀλλήλων
⟨ἰδίαν⟩ τιν᾽ ἔχουσι φύσιν, ὥσπερ καὶ αἱ τοὺς τῶν φυτῶν. ἀλλὰ μᾶλλον

46 [κριθή, εἶτα κόλλυβος, εἶτα] in uncis posuit Schwarze; vide commentarium ad loc.:
sine uncis Schneider, &c.: κριθὴν (κριθὴ CE) εἶτα κόλλυμβον (κόλυβον K²) εἶτα codd.
ἡμιωβόλιον coni. Tod: ἡμιόλιον ὄβολον ACEFKL: ἡμνόλιον ὄβολον M: ἡμιόλιον ὄκολον
DG: ἡ. ὄκολον N: ἡμιωβόλος Schneider, &c. 47 τὰ ἄνω ⟨τὰ⟩ Schneider. δὲ ὅτι E
Coraës: δέον ὅτι ceteri codd.: δὲ διότι Wimmer, Caley & Richards. τοῖς καύμασι] τοὶ
καύμασι E: τοῖς καύμασιν FL Aldus. τὸ δοκιμάζειν E Furlanus: τοῦ δοκιμάζειν ceteri:
δοκιμάζει Turnebus, Schneider, &c. ἐξ αὐτῆς ego: ἐξ αὐτῆς codd. ὑπολαμβάνεται
ego: ὑπολαμβάνει codd.: ὑπολαμβάνουσιν Coraës, Schneider, &c. ὡς ἰδίοντος τοῦ ἔδους
ignotus: vide commentarium ad loc.: ὡς ἴδιον τὸ τοῦ εἴδους cod.: ἴδιόν τι τοῦ ἔδους Coraës,
Schneider, &c. 48 σχεδόν om. Schneider, &c. μαλάττεσθαι Turnebus, Schneider,
&c.; cf. μαλάττεται infra: ἀλλοιοῦσθαι codd. ⟨ἅμα⟩ τοῖς χυτοῖς coni. Caley & Richards,
p. 55. λίθους codd.: πλίνθους Furlanus. οἷον ego: ὦν codd.: lacunam post συντιθεμένας
indicant Wimmer, Caley & Richards. ἁπάσας γὰρ] γὰρ om. Turnebus, Schneider.
49 ὑελίτιδος Hill e coni. Salmasii: ὑελίδος codd. ὥς τινές EFK²: οὔ τινές ceteri.
πυρώσει de Laet (in versione), Hill; cf. § 48, πυροῦντες: πυκνώσει codd. et ceteri edd.
χαλκῷ] χάλικι Hill e coni. de Laet. πρὸς γὰρ τῷ Turnebus: πρὸς γὰρ τὸ codd. ἔχει

together with the amount of precious metal contained in a stater of the alloy. Those concerned use streaks, starting with that which indicates the smallest amount of baser metal, this amount being [a krithe, then a kollybos, then] a quarter-obol or a half-obol. Thus the proportion of precious metal is detected from these streaks. 47. All stones of this kind are found in the river Tmolus. They are smooth in character, rather like counters, flat, but not circular: they are approximately twice the size of the largest counter. In testing the metal, the upper surface of the stone, which is exposed to the sun, differs from the lower surface and is superior to it in this respect. This is because the upper surface is also the drier, for moisture hinders the abstracting of the metal. Indeed in great heat the test is less satisfactory since the stone gives off moisture which renders it slippery. The same thing happens also to other stones, including those of which divine images are made; and this is taken to be an omen, as though the statue were sweating.

VIII. 48. These, then, are substantially the characteristic differences and powers of stones. Those belonging to earth are less numerous, but more peculiar. For earth indeed may undergo processes of (*a*) melting, (*b*) softening, and (*c*) hardening again. Thus (*a*) it melts, like stone, along with ores that are smelted, but (*b*) it is softened and (*c*) stones are made of it, for example the parti-coloured and the other kinds that are produced artificially. All of these are made by softening and firing earth. 49. And if, as some maintain, glass is made from vitreous earth, so too it is firing that causes this earth to become glass. A most peculiar earth is that which is mixed with copper, for it not merely melts and mingles with the metal, but also has a remarkable power of enhancing the beauty of its colour. In Cilicia there exists an earth which is heated and becomes viscous, and is used in place of birdlime for dressing vines as a protection against grubs. 50. One might try to find those distinctive qualities which render earth apt to harden to the consistency of stone. And yet those which give earths a distinctive flavour have a peculiar nature of their own no less than those which give a distinctive flavour to plants. It will be better, however, to enumerate the

C¹E *Turnebus*: ἔχειν *ceteri codd.* 50 εἴη *Turnebus*: ἤ ACDEFGKL: ἤ MN. τοὺς τούτων *codd.*: τοὺς τῶν τόπων *Turnebus (in versione), coni. Schneider*: τῶν τόπων *Wimmer, Caley & Richards.* ⟨ἰδίαν⟩ τιν᾽ ἔχουσι *Turnebus (in versione), Schneider*: τιν᾽ (τινὰ DN) ἔχουσαι *codd.*

ἄν τις αὐτὰς τοῖς χρώμασι διαριθμήσειεν οἷσπερ καὶ οἱ γραφεῖς
(40) χρῶνται. τὸ ὅλον ἐν τοῖς μετάλλοις πλεῖσται καὶ ἰδιώταται φύσεις
εὑρίσκονται τῶν τοιούτων, ὧν τὰ μέν ἐστι γῆς καθάπερ ὤχρα καὶ
μίλτος, τὰ δ᾽ οἷον ἄμμου καθάπερ χρυσοκόλλα καὶ κύανος, τὰ δὲ
50 κονίας οἷον σανδαράκη καὶ ἀρρενικὸν καὶ ὅσα ὅμοια τούτοις. καὶ γὰρ
ἡ γένεσις τούτων, ὥσπερ ἐξ ἀρχῆς εἴπομεν, ἤτοι συρροῆς τινος ἢ
διηθήσεως γινομένης. καὶ ἔνιά γε δὴ φαίνεται πεπυρωμένα καὶ οἷον
κατακεκαυμένα, οἷον καὶ ἡ σανδαράκη καὶ τὸ ἀρρενικὸν καὶ τὰ ἄλλα τὰ
τοιαῦτα. πάντα δ᾽ ὡς ἁπλῶς εἰπεῖν ἀπὸ τῆς ἀναθυμιάσεως ταῦτα τῆς
51 ξηρᾶς καὶ καπνώδους. εὑρίσκεται δὴ πάντ᾽ ἐν τοῖς μετάλλοις τοῖς
ἀργυρείοις τε καὶ χρυσείοις, ἔνια δὲ καὶ ἐν τοῖς χαλκωρυχείοις, οἷον
ἀρρενικόν, σανδαράκη, χρυσοκόλλα, μίλτος, ὤχρα, κύανος· ἐλάχιστος
δὲ οὗτος καὶ κατ᾽ ἐλάχιστα. τῶν δ᾽ ἄλλων τῶν μέν εἰσι ῥάβδοι, τὴν
δ᾽ ὤχραν ἀθρόαν πώς φασιν εἶναι· μίλτον δὲ παντοδαπὴν ὥστε εἰς τὰ
ἀνδρείκελα χρῆσθαι τοὺς γραφεῖς· καὶ ὤχραν ἀντ᾽ ἀρρενικοῦ διὰ τὸ
52 μηδὲν τῇ χρόᾳ διαφέρειν, δοκεῖν δέ. ἀλλὰ μίλτου τε καὶ ὤχρας ἐστὶν
ἐνιαχοῦ μέταλλα καὶ κατὰ ταὐτὰ καθάπερ ἐν Καππαδοκίᾳ, καὶ ὀρύτ-
τεται πολλή. χαλεπὸν δὲ τοῖς μεταλλεῦσί φασιν εἶναι τὸ πνίγεσθαι·
ταχὺ γὰρ καὶ ἐν ὀλίγῳ τοῦτο ποιεῖν. βελτίστη δὲ δοκεῖ μίλτος ἡ Κεία
εἶναι· γίνονται γὰρ πλείους. ἡ μὲν οὖν ἐκ τῶν μετάλλων, ἐπειδὴ καὶ
τὰ σιδηρεῖα ἔχει μίλτον. (53) ἐν δὲ τῷ μικρῷ ⟨μετάλλῳ⟩ μεταλλεύεται
καθ᾽ αὑτήν. (52) ἀλλὰ καὶ ἡ Λημνία καὶ ἣν καλοῦσι Σινωπικήν. αὕτη
53 δ᾽ ἐστὶν ἡ Καππαδοκική, κατάγεται δ᾽ εἰς Σινώπην. ἔστι δὲ αὐτῆς γένη
τρία, ἡ μὲν ἐρυθρὰ σφόδρα, ἡ δὲ ἔλευκος, ἡ δὲ μέση. ταύτην αὐτάρκη
καλοῦμεν διὰ τὸ μὴ μίγνυσθαι, τὰς δ᾽ ἑτέρας μιγνύουσι. γίνεται δὲ
καὶ ἐκ τῆς ὤχρας κατακαιομένης ἀλλὰ χείρων, τὸ δ᾽ εὕρημα Κυδίου.
συνεῖδε γὰρ ἐκεῖνος, ὥς φασι, κατακαυθέντος τινὸς παντοπωλίου τὴν
54 ὤχραν ἰδὼν ἡμίκαυστον καὶ πεφοινιγμένην. τιθέασι δ᾽ εἰς τὰς καμίνους

50 αὐτὰς (⟨αὐ⟩τὰς Wimmer, Caley & Richards) . . . διαριθμήσειεν Turnebus (in
versione), Schneider: τὰς . . . διαριθμήσεις (διαριθμήσις F) codd.: τοὺς . . . διαριθμήσειε
Furlanus. (§ 40) Post χρῶνται interposui § 40, τὸ ὅλον . . . ὅμοια τούτοις;
vide commentarium ad loc. τὸ ὅλον codd.: τὸ δὲ ὅλον Schneider. ἐστι ego: εἰσι codd.
ὤχρα Turnebus: ὤχρα codd., ceteri edd. τὰ δ᾽ οἷον EK²: τὰ δὲ οἷον Furlanus: τὸ δ᾽
οἷον ACDFGK¹LMN: τὰ δ᾽ ὧν BH. κύανος] add. E αὐτοφυὴς . . . χρυσοκόλλαν
rep. e § 39. 51 τε καὶ] τε om. F Aldus. ἔνια C²EFK²M: ἦια ceteri. χαλκωρυχείοις Turnebus: χαλκωρυχείοις codd., ceteri edd. ὤχρα Turnebus: ὤχρα codd., ceteri
edd. οὗτος] οὗ F. τῶν μέν εἰσι] τῶν μὲν ἥμισυ E. φασιν E Turnebus:
φαντασίαν ceteri. γραφεῖς Furlanus: βαφοῖς A: βαφεῖς ceteri. ὤχραν] ὤχραν codd.,
edd.: ὤχρα Turnebus (in versione). ἀρρενικοῦ EFK²M: ἐρρενικοῦ ceteri. 52 ἀλλὰ
Furlanus: τὰ ἄλλα CE: τἆλλα ceteri. ἐνιαχοῦ EFK²: ἐνισχοῦ ceteri. ταὐτὰ Turnebus
(in versione), Schneider, &c.: ταῦτα codd. μεταλλεῦσι Turnebus: μετάλλοις codd.
δοκεῖ Turnebus: ποιεῖ codd. σιδηρεῖα Schneider: σιδήρια codd. (53) ἐν δὲ τῷ
μικρῷ ⟨μετάλλῳ⟩ μεταλλεύεται καθ᾽ αὑτήν transtuli ex initio § 53, verbo μετάλλῳ

distinctive qualities of the earths with reference to the colours
used in painting pictures. (40.) In general, it is in mines that we
find the most numerous and most peculiar varieties of such
earths. Some of them, like ochre and ruddle, are composed of
earth, some, like chrysocolla and *cyanus*, of a kind of sand, and
some, like realgar and orpiment and so forth, of powder. 50. Their
formation, incidentally, is due either to a 'conflux' or to 'filtering',
as we stated at the beginning. Some of them at least have obviously undergone exposure to fire and some process of complete
combustion, as for example realgar, orpiment and the like; but it
may be stated generally that all are products of the dry and
smoky exhalation. 51. All these earths are found in silver-mines
and gold-mines, and some, like orpiment, realgar, chrysocolla,
ruddle, ochre and *cyanus*, in copper-mines also. *Cyanus* is the least
plentiful and is distributed in the smallest quantities. Of the rest,
some occur in veins, while we are told that ochre is found in
masses, and ruddle in every variety of shade: hence painters use
it for flesh-tints. Moreover, ochre is said to be a substitute for
orpiment since its colour is in no way different, but only appears
to be. 52. To proceed, there are some regions, Cappadocia for
instance, where ochre and ruddle are even mined in the same
place, and large quantities are dug. The miners, however, are
said to be hampered by the danger of suffocation, which may be
brought about rapidly or at any rate in a short time. The best
ruddle, for there are many varieties, appears to be that of Ceos,
some of which comes from the mines there, for iron-mines also
contain ruddle. (53) In the Little Mine, however, it is mined by
itself. 52. But there are also the Lemnian and the so-called
Sinopic, the latter being merely the Cappadocian, which is
brought down to Sinope. 53. There are three kinds of ruddle, one
deep-red, one pale, and one medium, the last being termed 'self-
sufficient', because, unlike the others, it does not need to be
mixed with anything. Ruddle of inferior quality is produced by
burning ochre. The invention belongs to Cydias, who is said to
have grasped it through noticing that, when a general store was
destroyed by fire, half-burnt ochre had turned crimson. 54. New

addito; vide commentarium ad loc. τῷ μικρῷ] τῇ Λήμνῳ *Furlanus (in versione), Hill.*
52 Λημνία *Turnebus (in versione), Heinsius:* λιμνία *codd.* καὶ ἦν καλοῦσι Σινωπικήν
Turnebus (in versione), Furlanus: ἦν καλοῦσιν ὠπτικὴν (ὀπτικὴν E) *codd.* 53 ἔστι
δὲ] δὲ *om.* F. γένη EFK²M: γεννή *ceteri.* μιγνύουσι EK²: μισθοῦσι *ceteri.* δὲ καὶ ἐκ
Schneider, &c.: τ' ἐκ *codd.* ὤχρας FK²M: χώρας *ceteri* κατακαυθέντος
CEFKLM: κα//καυθέντος A: κα καυθέντος G: καὶ καυθέντος D: κατὰ καυθέντος N.
παντοπωλίου *Turnebus:* παντωλίου ACDEFGK¹LMN: πανδοχείου K² *Furlanus,
Wimmer, Caley & Richards.* πεφοινιγμένην] φοινιγμένην DJ.

χύτρας καινὰς περιπλάσαντες πηλῷ· ὀπτῶσι γὰρ διάπυροι γινόμεναι·
ὅσῳ δ' ἂν μᾶλλον πυρωθῶσι, τοσούτῳ μᾶλλον μελαντέραν καὶ ἀνθρα-
κωδεστέραν ποιοῦσι. μαρτυρεῖ δ' ἡ γένεσις αὐτή· δόξειε γὰρ ἂν ὑπὸ
πυρὸς ἅπαντα ταῦτα μεταβάλλειν, εἴπερ ὁμοίαν ἢ παραπλησίαν δεῖ τὴν
55 ἐνταῦθα τῇ φυσικῇ νομίζειν. ἔστι δέ, ὥσπερ καὶ μίλτος ἡ μὲν αὐτό-
ματος ἡ δὲ τεχνική, καὶ κύανος ὁ μὲν αὐτοφυὴς ὁ δὲ σκευαστὸς ὥσπερ
ἐν Αἰγύπτῳ. γένη δὲ κυάνου τρία, ὁ Αἰγύπτιος, καὶ ⟨ὁ⟩ Σκύθης, καὶ
τρίτος ὁ Κύπριος. βέλτιστος δ' ὁ Αἰγύπτιος εἰς τὰ ἄκρατα λειώματα,
ὁ δὲ Σκύθης εἰς τὰ ὑδαρέστερα. σκευαστὸς δ' ὁ Αἰγύπτιος. καὶ οἱ
γράφοντες τὰ περὶ τοὺς βασιλεῖς καὶ τοῦτο γράφουσι, τίς πρῶτος
βασιλεὺς ἐποίησε χυτὸν κύανον μιμησάμενος τὸν αὐτοφυῆ, δῶρά τε
πέμπεσθαι παρ' ἄλλων τε καὶ ἐκ Φοινίκης φόρον κυάνου, τοῦ μὲν
ἀπύρου τοῦ δὲ πεπυρωμένου. φασὶ δ' οἱ τὰ φάρμακα τρίβοντες τὸν
Σκύθην κύανον ἐξ ἑαυτοῦ ποιεῖν χρώματα τέτταρα, τὸ μὲν πρῶτον ἐκ
τῶν λεπτοτάτων λευκότατον, τὸ δὲ δεύτερον ἐκ τῶν παχυτάτων μελάν-
56 τατον. ταῦτά τε δὴ τέχνῃ γίνεται καὶ ἔτι τὸ ψιμύθιον. τίθεται γὰρ
μόλυβδος ὑπὲρ ὄξους ἐν πίθοις ἡλίκον πλίνθος. ὅταν δὲ λάβῃ πάχος,
λαμβάνει δὲ μάλιστα ἐν ἡμέραις δέκα, τότ' ἀνοίγουσιν, εἶτ' ἀπο-
ξύουσιν ὥσπερ εὐρῶτά τινα ἀπ' αὐτοῦ, καὶ πάλιν τιθέασι καὶ πάλιν,
ἕως ἂν καταναλώσωσι. τὸ δ' ἀποξυόμενον ἐν τριπτῆρι τρίβουσι καὶ
57 ἀπηθοῦσιν ἀεί, τὸ δ' ἔσχατον ὑφιστάμενόν ἐστι τὸ ψιμύθιον. παραπλησίως δὲ καὶ ὁ ἰὸς γίνεται· χαλκὸς γὰρ ἐρυθρὸς ὑπὲρ τρυγὸς τίθεται
καὶ ἀποξύεται τὸ ἐπιγινόμενον αὐτῷ, ⟨ἐπεὶ⟩ ἐπιφαίνεται γινόμενος ⟨ὁ
58 ἰός⟩. γίνεται δὲ καὶ κιννάβαρι τὸ μὲν αὐτοφυὲς τὸ δὲ κατ' ἐργασίαν.
αὐτοφυὲς μὲν τὸ περὶ Ἰβηρίαν σκληρὸν σφόδρα καὶ λιθῶδες, καὶ τὸ ἐν
Κόλχοις. τοῦτο δέ φασιν εἶναι ⟨ἐπὶ⟩ κρημνῶν, ὃ καταβάλλουσι τοξεύ-
οντες. τὸ δὲ κατ' ἐργασίαν ὑπὲρ Ἐφέσου μικρὸν ⟨ἐν Κιλβιανοῖς (?)⟩
ἐξ ἑνὸς τόπου μόνον. ἔστι δ' ἄμμος ἣν συλλέγουσι λαμπυρίζουσαν

54 καινὰς Turnebus: κενὰς ACDEGKLMN: λενὰς F Aldus.   πηλῷ Turnebus: πολὺν
codd.   ὀπτῶσι F Aldus: ὀπτῶσαι ceteri.   γινόμεναι] γενόμεναι Schneider, &c.
μαρτυρεῖ δ' Schneider, &c.: μαρτυρεῖ δ' ἂν codd.   αὐτή Schneider, &c.: αὐτὸ codd.
γὰρ ἂν Turnebus: γὰρ τὸ codd.   μεταβάλλειν] μεταβαλεῖν Schneider, &c.   τῇ φυσικῇ]
τὴν φυσικὴ E: τῇ φυσικῇ ⟨γενέσει⟩ Schneider.   55 ⟨ὁ⟩ Σκύθης ego.   χυτὸν] τεχνητὸν
Furlanus.   φόρον E Turnebus: φόρου codd.   τὸν Σκύθην ego: τὸν μὲν codd.   λευκότατον
Turnebus, Caley & Richards: λεπτότατον codd., Wimmer.   τῶν παχυτάτων] τῶν om.
Turnebus, Wimmer.   56 μόλυβδος Wimmer: μόλιβδος codd.   ἡλίκον πλίνθος post
πίθοις Schneider: ἡλίκον πλίνθος post πάχος Turnebus: ἡλίκον πλῆθος post πάχος codd.
εὐρῶτά] εὐρῶτι FL Aldus.   καὶ πάλιν τιθέασι καὶ πάλιν] καὶ πάλιν FKLM Aldus: καὶ
πάλιν ⟨τιθέασι⟩ Schneider.   ἀπηθοῦσιν ego; cf. H.P. 9. 8. 4: ἀφιθοῦσιν ACDGKLMN:
α θοῦσιν E: ἀφηθοῦσιν Schneider: ἐφθοῦσιν F Aldus.   ψιμύθιον Heinsius: ψιμίθιον
codd.   57 γίνεται] γίγνεται E.   τρυγὸς E: τριγὸς ceteri.   αὐτῷ, ⟨ἐπεὶ⟩ ἐπιφαίνεται γινόμενος ⟨ὁ ἰός⟩ ego: οὕτω ἐπιφαίνεται τιθέμενος codd.: αὐτῷ· ἐπιφαίνεται
γὰρ ὁ ἰός Wimmer, Caley & Richards: οὕτω δ' ἐπιφαίνεται ὁ ἰὸς τιθεμένου Schneider.

pots luted with clay are placed in a furnace. When the pots are thoroughly exposed to the fire, they cause the ochre to be baked, and the more they are burnt, the darker and more glowing the ochre becomes. The process of generation testifies to the truth of this. For fire would appear to be the agent responsible for all these transformations if we are to suppose the process employed here to be similar to, or comparable with, the natural process of generation. 55. Just as there is a natural and an artificial ruddle, so too there is a natural and a prepared *cyanus*, such as is made in Egypt. There are three kinds of *cyanus*, the Egyptian, the Scythian, and lastly the Cyprian, the Egyptian being best for undiluted pigment-powders and the Scythian for the diluted. The Egyptian is a preparation; and the records relating to the kings include the name of the first king to produce fused 'cyanus' in imitation of the natural kind, together with the information that along with gifts tribute came from Phoenicia and elsewhere in the form of *cyanus*, some of which had been fired and some not. Grinders of paints assert that four shades can be produced from the Scythian *cyanus* by itself, the first shade, which is also the palest, being made from the finest particles, while the second, which is the darkest, is prepared from the coarsest. Besides these, white lead also is produced artificially. 56. A piece of lead as big as a brick is placed above some vinegar in a cask. When after about ten days the lead has acquired thickness, the cask is opened and a kind of mildew scraped from the lead, which is repeatedly placed in this way until it is used up. The scrapings are pounded in a mortar and continually strained away; and the white lead is the matter finally left deposited. 57. Verdigris is produced in a comparable manner. Copper is placed above wine-lees, and the substance that forms on it is scraped away, for the verdigris, as it forms, appears on the surface of the copper. 58. There is also natural and manufactured cinnabar. Spanish cinnabar, which is extremely hard and stony, is natural, and so too is that of Colchis, which is said to be found on precipices and shot down by arrows. The manufactured variety comes from one place only, which is a little above Ephesus (in the territory of the Cilbians?). Here a sand which glows like the scarlet kermes-berry is collected

---

80 THEOPHRASTUS

καθάπερ ὁ κόκκος· ταύτην δὲ τρίψαντες ὅλως ἐν ἀγγείοις λιθίνοις
λειοτάτην πλύνουσιν ἐν χαλκοῖς [μικρὸν ἐν καλοῖς], τὸ δ᾽ ὑφιστάμενον πάλιν λαβόντες πλύνουσι καὶ τρίβουσιν, ἐν ᾧπέρ ἐστι τὸ τῆς
τέχνης· οἱ μὲν γὰρ ἐκ τοῦ ἴσου πολὺ περιποιοῦσιν, οἱ δ᾽ ὀλίγον ἢ
οὐθέν· ἀλλὰ πλύσματι ⟨τῷ⟩ ἐπάνω χρῶνται ἐν πρὸς ἓν ἀλείφοντες.
γίνεται δὲ τὸ μὲν ὑφιστάμενον κάτω κιννάβαρι, τὸ δ᾽ ἐπάνω καὶ πλεῖον
59 πλύσμα. καταδεῖξαι δέ φασι καὶ εὑρεῖν τὴν ἐργασίαν Καλλίαν τινὰ
Ἀθηναῖον ἐκ τῶν ἀργυρείων, ὃς οἰόμενος ἔχειν τὴν ἄμμον χρυσίον διὰ
τὸ λαμπυρίζειν ἐπραγματεύετο καὶ συνέλεγεν. ἐπεὶ δ᾽ ᾔσθετο ὅτι οὐκ
ἔχοι τὸ δὲ τῆς ἄμμου κάλλος ἐθαύμαζε διὰ τὴν χρόαν, οὕτως ἐπὶ τὴν
ἐργασίαν ἦλθε ταύτην. οὐ παλαιὸν δ᾽ ἐστὶν ἀλλὰ περὶ ἔτη μάλιστ᾽
60 ἐνενήκοντα εἰς ἄρχοντα Πραξίβουλον Ἀθήνησι. φανερὸν δ᾽ ἐκ τούτων
ὅτι μιμεῖται τὴν φύσιν ἡ τέχνη, τὰ δ᾽ ἴδια ποιεῖ, καὶ τούτων τὰ μὲν
χρήσεως χάριν τὰ δὲ μόνον φαντασίας ὥσπερ τὰς ἀλοιφάς. ἔνια δὲ
ἴσως ἀμφοῖν ὥσπερ χυτὸν ἄργυρον. ἔστι γάρ τις χρεία καὶ τούτου.
ποιεῖται δὲ ὅταν ⟨κιννάβαρι⟩ τριφθῇ μετ᾽ ὄξους ἐν ἀγγείῳ χαλκῷ καὶ
δοίδυκι χαλκῷ. τὰ μὲν οὖν τοιαῦτα τάχ᾽ ἄν τις λάβοι πλείω.

61 IX. Τῶν δὲ μεταλλευτῶν τὰ ἐν τοῖς γεωφανέσιν ἔτι λοιπά, [περὶ]
ὧν ἡ γένεσις ὥσπερ ἐλέχθη κατ᾽ ἀρχὰς ἐκ συρροῆς τινος καὶ ἐκκρίσεως
γίνεται καθαρωτέρας καὶ ὁμαλωτέρας τῶν ἄλλων. χρώματα δὲ παντοῖα
λαμβάνουσι καὶ διὰ τὴν τῶν ὑποκειμένων ⟨φύσιν καὶ (?)⟩ διὰ τὴν τῶν
⟨ποι⟩ούντων διαφοράν, ἐξ ὧν τὰς μὲν μαλάττοντες, τὰς δὲ τήκοντες
καὶ τρίβοντες συντιθέασι τὰς λίθους τὰς ἐκ τῆς Ἀσίας ταύτας ἀγομένας.
62 αἱ δ᾽ αὐτοφυεῖς καὶ ἅμα τῷ περιττῷ τὸ χρήσιμον ἔχουσαι σχεδὸν τρεῖς
εἰσιν ἢ τέτταρες, ἥ τε Μηλιὰς καὶ ἡ Κιμωλία καὶ ἡ Σαμία καὶ ἡ
Τυμφαϊκὴ τετάρτη παρὰ ταύτας ἢ γύψος. χρῶνται δὲ οἱ γραφεῖς τῇ
Μηλιάδι μόνον, τῇ Σαμίᾳ δ᾽ οὔ, καίπερ οὔσῃ καλῇ, διὰ τὸ λίπος ἔχειν
καὶ πυκνότητα καὶ λειότητα. τὸ γὰρ ἠρέμα τραχῶδες καὶ ἀλιπὲς ἐπὶ

58 κόκκος] κρόκκος D: κρόκος J.   ὅλως] ὅλλως LN.   πλύνουσιν] πλατύνουσιν E.
[μικρὸν ἐν καλοῖς] in uncis posuerunt Schneider, &c.; cf. supra μικρὸν ⟨ἐν Κιλβιανοῖς?⟩.
οἱ μὲν γὰρ] οἱ μὲν καὶ F Aldus, Turnebus.   ⟨τῷ⟩ ἐπάνω Schneider, &c.   59 ἔχοι A;
cf. H.P. 9. 18. 4: ἔχει ceteri.   μάλιστ᾽ F Aldus: μάλισθ᾽ ceteri.   Ἀθήνησι] Ἀθήνῃσι edd.
60 μιμεῖται] ⟨τὰ μὲν⟩ μιμεῖται Schneider.   χρήσεως] ἀχρήσεως D.   ἀλοιφάς coni.
Caley & Richards: ἄλπεις codd.   χρεία Furlanus: χρόα codd.   ὅταν ⟨κιννάβαρι⟩
ego: ὅταν τί* codd.: ὅταν τὸ ⟨κιννάβαρι⟩ Schneider, &c.   δοίδυκι C²F Aldus: δίδυκι
C¹DGKLMN: δοιδίκι E: δύδυκι A.   61 γεωφανέσιν] γεωφανέσι Wimmer.   [περὶ]
ὧν: περὶ in uncis posuerunt Schneider, &c.   ὑποκειμένων ⟨φύσιν καὶ?⟩ ego.   ποιούντων
Turnebus: *ούντων codd.   τὰς μὲν ... τὰς δὲ] τὰ μὲν ... τὰ δὲ E.   μαλάττοντες
Turnebus (in versione), Schneider, &c.: μελαντῶντες codd.   62 Μηλιὰς de Laet:
μιλιὰς codd.   Τυμφαϊκὴ Turnebus: στυμφαϊκὴ codd.   τετάρτη Hill: καὶ τετάρτη codd.
παρὰ ταύτας Turnebus: περὶ ταύτας codd.   ἢ γύψος ACN: ἡ γύψος DEFGKLM.
Μηλιάδι μόνον de Laet e coni. Salmasii: μιλία διὰ μόνον codd.   τῇ Σαμίᾳ Turnebus:

and thoroughly pounded to a very fine powder in stone vessels. It is then washed in copper vessels, and the sediment is taken and pounded and washed again. There is a knack in doing this, for from an equal quantity of material some workers secure a great amount of cinnabar, and others little or none. However, use is made of the washings floating above, particularly as a wall-paint. The sediment which forms below turns out to be cinnabar, while all that is above, which is the greater part, is merely washings. 59. The process is said to have been invented and introduced by Callias, an Athenian from the silver-mines, who collected and studied the sand, thinking that it contained gold owing to its glowing appearance. But when he found that it contained no gold, he still admired its fine colour and so came to discover the process, which is by no means an old one, but dates back only some ninety years before the archonship of Praxibulus at Athens. 60. From these examples it is clear that Art imitates Nature, and yet produces its own peculiar substances, some for their utility, some merely for their appearance, like wall-paint, and some for both purposes, like quicksilver; for even this has its uses. It is made by pounding cinnabar with vinegar in a copper mortar with a copper pestle. And perhaps one could find several things of this kind.

IX. 61. However, among earths which are mined there still remain those that are found in earth-pits. These are generated, as was said at the beginning, from a 'conflux' or 'secretion' of exceptional purity and uniformity. Colours of every kind are derived from them owing to the nature of the substances themselves, and also to differences in their manufacture (?). These stones that are brought from Asia are composed of such earths, some of these earths being softened for the purpose and others ground and melted. 62. There are, roughly speaking, three or four natural earths which are useful as well as unusual, namely the Melian, the Cimolian, the Samian, and finally besides these the Tymphaic, otherwise known as 'gypsum'. Only the Melian is used in painting pictures, no use being made of Samian in spite of its beautiful appearance, because it is greasy, dense, and smooth. Moderate roughness and an absence of grease are more suitable

τῆς μίας codd.   ἠρέμα τραχῶδες ego: ἀραιὸν καὶ ἠρέμα τραχῶδες coni. Salmasius: ἤρεμον καὶ *δες codd.   ἀλιπὲς] ἐλλιπὲς C: ἐλλειπὲς E.

τῆς γραφῆς ἁρμόττει μᾶλλον, ὅπερ ἡ Μηλιὰς ἔχει ⟨ἅμα⟩ τῷ ψαφαρῷ.
63 εἰσὶ ⟨δὲ⟩ καὶ ἐν τῇ Μήλῳ καὶ ἐν τῇ Σάμῳ διαφοραὶ τῆς γῆς πλείους.
ὀρύττοντα μὲν οὖν οὐκ ἔστιν ὀρθὸν στῆναι ἐν τοῖς ἐν Σάμῳ ἀλλ'
ἀναγκαῖον ἢ ὕπτιον ἢ πλάγιον. ἡ δὲ φλὲψ ἐπὶ πολὺ διατείνει, τὸ μὲν
ὕψος ἡλίκον δίπους, τὸ δὲ βάθος πολλῷ μείζων· ἐφ' ἑκάτερα δ' αὐτὴν
λίθοι περιέχουσιν ἐξ ὧν ἐξαιρεῖται. διαφυὴν ἔχει διὰ μέσου, καὶ ἡ
διαφυὴ βελτίων ἐστὶ τῶν ἔξω, καὶ πάλιν ἑτέραν τοιαύτην καὶ ἑτέραν
⟨τρίτην⟩ ἄχρι τεττάρων. βελτίστη δ' ἡ ἐσχάτη, ⟨ἣ⟩ καλεῖται ἀστήρ·
64 χρῶνται δὲ τῇ γῇ πρὸς τὰ ἱμάτια μάλιστ' ἢ μόνον. χρῶνται δὲ τῇ
Τυμφαϊκῇ πρὸς τὰ ἱμάτια καὶ καλοῦσι γύψον οἱ περὶ Θετταλίαν τε καὶ
τοὺς τόπους ἐκείνους. ἡ δὲ γύψος γίνεται πλείστη μὲν ἐν Κύπρῳ καὶ
περιφανεστάτη. μικρὸν γὰρ ἀφαιροῦσι τῆς γῆς ὀρύττοντες. ἐν Φοινίκῃ
δὲ καὶ ἐν Συρίᾳ καίοντες τοὺς λίθους ποιοῦσιν. ἔπειτα δ' ἐν Θουρίοις·
καὶ γὰρ ἐκεῖ γίνεται πολλή. τρίτη δὲ ἡ περὶ Τυμφαίαν καὶ περὶ
65 Περραιβίαν καὶ κατ' ἄλλους τόπους. ἡ δὲ φύσις αὐτῶν ἰδία· λιθωδε-
στέρα γὰρ μᾶλλόν ἐστιν ἢ γεώδης· ὁ δὲ λίθος ἐμφερὴς τῷ ἀλαβαστρίτῃ·
μέγας δ' οὐ τέμνεται ἀλλὰ χαλικώδης. ἡ δὲ γλισχρότης καὶ θερμότης
ὅταν βρεχθῇ θαυμαστή. χρῶνται γὰρ πρός τε τὰ οἰκοδομήματα αὐτῷ
τῷ λίθῳ περιχέοντες κἄν τι ἄλλο βούλωνται τοιοῦτο κολλῆσαι.
66 κόψαντες δὲ καὶ ὕδωρ ἐπιχέοντες ταράττουσι ξύλοις, τῇ χειρὶ γὰρ οὐ
δύνανται διὰ τὴν θερμότητα. βρέχουσι δὲ παραχρῆμα πρὸς τὴν χρείαν·
ἐὰν γὰρ μικρὸν πρότερον ταχὺ πήγνυται καὶ οὐκ ἔστι διελεῖν. θαυμαστὴ δὲ καὶ ἡ ἰσχύς· ὅτε γὰρ οἱ λίθοι ῥήγνυνται καὶ διαφέρονται, ἡ
δὲ οὐδαμῶς ἀνίησι, πολλάκις δὲ καὶ τὰ μὲν πέπτωκε καὶ ὑφήρηται, τὰ
67 δ' ἄνω κρεμάμενα μένει συνεχόμενα τῇ κολλήσει. δύναται δὲ καὶ

---

62 Μηλιὰς de Laet: μιλιὰς codd. ⟨ἅμα⟩ τῷ ψαφαρῷ ego: ἐν τῷ ψαφαρῷ coni.
Schneider: τῷ φαριδ' ACDGJKLMN: το φαρ*δ' E: τῷ φαρίδι F Aldus. 63 εἰσὶ
⟨δὲ⟩ καὶ ego: ἐστὶ καὶ codd.: εἰσὶ δὲ de Laet, Schneider, &c. διαφοραὶ . . . Σάμῳ
om. N. στῆναι Schneider: στῆσαι codd. τὸ μὲν FL Aldus: τὰ μὲν ceteri. ἡλίκον ego:
ἡλίκην codd.: ἡλίκη Furlanus. δίπους Turnebus: διπλοῦς ACDEFGKLMN. λίθοι]
κίθοι F Aldus. περιέχουσιν Furlanus: περιέξουσιν codd. διαφυὴν Turnebus (in versione), Furlanus: διαφύειν codd. βελτίων Furlanus: βέλτιον codd. τοιαύτην ego: αὐτῇ
A: αὐτῇ ceteri: αὐτῆς Furlanus. ἑτέραν ⟨τρίτην⟩ ἄχρι ego: ἑτέραν* ταχρη (ταχρη
om. E: ταχη F) codd.: ἑτέραν ἄχρι Furlanus. βελτίστη δ' ego: ἔστιν codd.: lacunam
ante ἔστιν indicant Schneider, &c. ἐσχάτη, ⟨ἣ⟩ ego. 64 μάλιστ' . . . ἱμάτια om.
DJN. ⟨ἣ μόνον⟩ Κιμωλίᾳ Hill e coni. de Laet. χρῶνται δὲ] χρῶνται δὲ ⟨καὶ⟩
Schneider: χ. δ. καὶ Wimmer, Caley & Richards. Τυμφαϊκῇ Turnebus: τυφικῇ
AEFGKLM: τυφικῆς C. Θετταλίαν τε ego: θεάτων δὲ codd.: τε Ἄθων Turne-
bus: τὸν Ἄθων Schneider, &c. Τυμφαίαν Furlanus: τύμφετον ACDEN: τύμφεται
FGK¹LM: Τέμπη φύεται K². Περραιβίαν Schneider: περαιβίαν FK² Aldus: περεβίαν
ACDEK¹LMN: περεκίαν G. 65 αὐτῶν codd.: αὐτῆς Turnebus, Schneider, &c.
ἀλαβαστρίτῃ EF edd.: ἀλαβάστριτι KLM: ἀλαβάστριτις C: ἀλάβαστριτις ADG: ἀλά-
βαστρίτις N. χαλικώδης Furlanus: χαλκώδης codd.: πλακώδης Turnebus. βρεχθῇ

in painting, and these, together with a loose texture, are the qualities possessed by Melian earth. 63. The earths of Melos and Samos differ in many more respects. A worker in the Samian pits cannot stand upright while digging, but is forced to lie on his back or side. The vein there stretches a considerable distance and is only about two feet in height, although its depth is much greater. On either side the earth is enclosed by rocks, from which it is extracted. The vein has running through the middle of it a seam, which is superior in quality to the outer parts, and again a second seam like the first, and a third and a fourth, the last, which is known as 'the Star', being the best. 64. The earth is used mainly, if not entirely, for treating cloaks. The same use is made of Tymphaic earth, which is called 'gypsum' by the people of Thessaly and the neighbourhood. Gypsum is most plentiful and most easily discerned in Cyprus, for only a little soil need be removed when it is dug there. In Phoenicia and Syria it is produced by the burning of stones, and again at Thurii, where large quantities are forthcoming. Thirdly there is the gypsum of Tymphaea, Perrhaebia and other places. 65. The nature of the varieties of gypsum is peculiar in that it is stony rather than earthy, the stone being similar to *alabastrites*, except that it is nodular and so cannot be hewn in large pieces. The viscidity and heat of gypsum, when it is moistened, are remarkable. It is used in building, being poured round the stones themselves, and is also applied to any similar material which requires bonding. 66. The workmen break it up, and then pour water over it and stir it with sticks, for they cannot do so by hand owing to the heat. It is moistened immediately before use, for if it is prepared even a little beforehand, it hardens rapidly and cannot be split up. Its strength too is remarkable, so much so that when the stones of a building break and come apart, the gypsum does not in any way relax its hold upon them. Indeed, often parts of a building have collapsed and have been taken away, while the upper portions remain suspended, being held together by the bonding of the gypsum. 67. Gypsum, moreover, can be removed, and so be rebaked and

Turnebus: ἐρεχθῇ ACDFGKLMN: ὀρυχθῇ E.   αὐτῷ τῷ λίθῳ *ego*: τοῦτον τὸν λίθον *codd.*, *edd.* (τοῦτον *in uncis posuit Schneider, om. Wimmer*).   περιχέοντες *Turnebus* (*in versione*), *Schneider*, &c.: περιέχοντες *codd.*   τοιοῦτο] τοιοῦτον *Schneider, Wimmer.* 66 ἐὰν γὰρ E: ἐὰν *ceteri; an recte?* ἐὰν ⟨δὲ⟩ *Schneider*, &c.   διελεῖν *Schneider*: διελθεῖν *codd.*   θαυμαστὴ δὲ E *Schneider* (*in suppl.*), *Wimmer, Caley & Richards*: θαῦμά ἐστι δὲ *ceteri.*   ἡ ἰσχύς EF: ἰσχύς *ceteri.*: ⟨ἡ⟩ ἰσχύς *Schneider*, &c.   ὅτε γὰρ] ὅτε τε F *Aldus.*   καὶ διαφέρονται] ἢ διαφέρονται *Schneider* (*in suppl.*), *Wimmer, Caley & Richards.*   ἡ δὲ οὐδαμῶς *ego*: ἡ δὲ ο*μος A: ἡ δὲ *μος CDFGKLMN: ἡ δὲ E: ἡ δεσμὸς *Turnebus*: ἡ γύψος *Schneider* (*in suppl.*), *Wimmer, Caley & Richards*.   μένει *Coraës*: καὶ *codd.*   67 δύναται] δύνανται FKLM.

84 THEOPHRASTUS

ὑφαιρουμένη πάλιν καὶ πάλιν ὀπτᾶσθαι καὶ γίνεσθαι χρησίμη. περὶ μὲν
οὖν Κύπρον καὶ Φοινίκην εἰς ταῦτα μάλιστα, περὶ δὲ Ἰταλίαν καὶ εἰς τὸν
οἶνον· καὶ οἱ γραφεῖς ⟨εἰς⟩ ἔνια τῶν κατὰ τὴν τέχνην, ἔτι δὲ οἱ κναφεῖς
ἐμπάττοντες εἰς τὰ ἱμάτια. διαφέρειν δὲ δοκεῖ καὶ πρὸς τὰ ἀπομάγματα
πολὺ τῶν ἄλλων, εἰς ὃ καὶ χρῶνται μᾶλλον καὶ μάλισθ᾽ οἱ περὶ τὴν
68 Ἑλλάδα, γλισχρότητι καὶ λειότητι. ἡ μὲν δύναμις ἐν τούτοις καὶ τοῖς
τοιούτοις. ἡ δὲ φύσις ἔοικεν ἀμφότερά πως ἔχειν καὶ τὰ τῆς κονίας
καὶ τὰ τῆς γῆς, θερμότητα καὶ γλισχρότητα, μᾶλλον δὲ ἑκατέρας
ὑπερεχούσας. θερμοτέρα γὰρ τῆς κονίας, γλισχροτέρα δὲ πολὺ τῆς
γῆς. ὅτι δ᾽ ἔμπυρος κἀκεῖθεν φανερόν. ἤδη γάρ τις ναῦς ἱματηγὸς
69 βρεχθέντων ἱματίων ὡς ἐπυρώθησαν συγκατεκαύθη καὶ αὐτή. ποιοῦσι
δὲ καὶ ἐν Φοινίκῃ καὶ ἐν Συρίᾳ καμινεύοντες αὐτήν καὶ καίοντες·
καίουσι δὲ μάλιστα τοὺς μαρμάρους καὶ ἁπλῶς τοὺς στερεωτάτους,
βόλιτον παρατιθέντες ἕνεκα τοῦ θᾶττον καίεσθαι καὶ μᾶλλον. δοκεῖ
γὰρ θερμότατον εἶναι πυρωθὲν καὶ πλεῖστον χρόνον διαμένει. ὀπτή-
σαντες δὲ κόπτουσιν ὥσπερ τὴν κονίαν. ἐκ τούτων δ᾽ ἂν δόξειεν εἶναι
φανερὸν ὅτι πυρώδης τις ἡ γένεσις αὐτῆς τὸ ὅλον ἐστίν.

67 ὑφαιρούμενη Ε: ὑφαιρομένη ceteri.   καὶ πάλιν Turnebus: καὶ πα* codd.   Post
περὶ μὲν οὖν desinit Ε.   μάλιστα] μάλιστα ⟨χρῶνται⟩ Schneider.   τὸν οἶνον Turnebus:
τὸν οἰκεῖον codd.: τὴν κονίασιν Hill e coni. Salmasii.   οἱ γραφεῖς ⟨εἰς⟩ Wimmer (Didot),
Caley & Richards: οἱ γραφεῖς ⟨πρὸς⟩ Schneider, Wimmer (Teubner).   κναφεῖς] γναφεῖς Μ
Wimmer.   τὰ ἀπομάγματα] τὰ om. Schneider, Wimmer.   καὶ μάλισθ᾽ FKLM edd.: ἡ μά-
λισθ᾽ ACDGN.   γλισχρότητι Turnebus: *χρότητι codd. (ὠχρότητι C²).   68 ἡ μὲν]
ἡ μὲν ⟨οὖν⟩ Schneider.   τοῖς τοιούτοις] τοῖς om. Schneider, Wimmer.   καὶ τὰ τῆς κονίας
Schneider: καὶ κατὰ τῆς κονίας codd.   καὶ τὰ τῆς γῆς] καὶ κατὰ τῆς γῆς C.   ἑκατέρας
ὑπερεχούσας codd.; cf. § 3 : ἑκατέραν ὑπερέχουσαν Schneider, &c.   θερμοτέρα ... γῆς
om. Schneider, Wimmer; etiam Caley & Richards, qui tamen in apparatu indicant.   ἔμπυρος
FKLM: ἔμπειρος ACDGN.   ἱματηγὸς Κ²: ἱματιγὸς ceteri.   αὐτή Κ: αὕτη ceteri.
69. ποιοῦσι ego: καίουσι codd.   καὶ καίοντες in uncis posuerunt Schneider, &c.   καὶ
ἁπλῶς τοὺς στερεωτάτους coni. Schneider: καὶ ἁπλουστέρους, στερεωτάτους codd.   βόλιτον παρατιθέντες ἕνεκα ego; vide commentarium ad loc.: μὲν παρατιθέντες *τα codd. (μ. π.
ἕνεκα Turnebus) : μὲν παρατιθέντες ⟨βόλιτον ἕνεκα⟩ Schneider, &c.   τούτων ACDGN:
τούτου F edd.: τούτω KLM.   ὅτι F Furlanus: ὅτι τὸ codd. (τὸ castigat Κ).   αὐτῆς
Schneider: αὐτὴ ACDFGJKLM: αὐτὴ Ν.

used again and again. In Cyprus and Phoenicia it is employed mainly for this purpose, but in Italy for preserving wine as well. Furthermore, it is used by painters for certain features of their art and by fullers for sprinkling on cloaks. In viscidity and smoothness it seems to be unequalled for taking the impressions of seals and this is the purpose for which it is largely, if not mainly, used in Greece. 68. It is in these and similar uses that the effectivenes of gypsum is shown. Its nature is such that it seems in some way to combine the qualities of lime and of earth, namely heat and viscidity; or rather, it possesses each in a superior degree, being hotter than lime and much more viscous than earth. That it contains fire is shown by the fact that on occasion a ship has been laden with cloaks which, becoming soaked, have caught fire, thus causing a conflagration which has destroyed the ship itself as well. 69. Both in Phoenicia and in Syria gypsum is made by being burnt in a furnace. For the most part 'marble', and moreover the hardest 'marble' available, is burnt, ox-dung being placed by it to make it burn more quickly and thoroughly. For once it has been kindled, ox-dung seems to be extremely hot and lasts for a very long time. When the material has been baked, it is broken up like lime. From these facts it seems clear that gypsum as a whole is generated by fire.

COMMENTARY

CHAPTER I

§ 1. ἐν τῇ γῇ means 'within the earth', as is clear from Arist. *Mete.* 341ᵇ9, τὴν μὲν τοῦ ἐν τῇ γῇ καὶ ἐπὶ τῇ γῇ ὑγροῦ ἀτμίδα. In the *De Lapidibus* Theophrastus is concerned only with substances that are formed *underground*. For his phrasing, cf. Plato, *Soph.* 265c, ὅσα τ᾽ ἐπὶ γῆς ἐκ σπερμάτων καὶ ῥιζῶν φύεται καὶ ὅσα ἄψυχα ἐν γῇ ξυνίσταται τηκτὰ (metals) καὶ ἄτηκτα (minerals). In this opening section γῆ is used in three senses, that of (*a*) earth as opposed, for example, to heaven (τῶν ἐν τῇ γῇ συνισταμένων), (*b*) earth as opposed to the other elements, fire, air, and water (τὰ δὲ γῆς), and (*c*) earth as opposed to stone (εἴ τινες δὴ τῆς γῆς αὐτῆς, κτλ.).

ὕδατος μὲν τὰ μεταλλευόμενα . . . γῆς δὲ λίθος. The view that water is the constituent of metals and earth the constituent of stones appears first in Plato (*Timaeus* 59a–b, 60b–c). It is also implicit in Aristotle's distinction between metals and 'fossiles'. See pp. 16–17.

γῆς δὲ λίθος . . . δυνάμει. Theophrastus states that earth is the constituent of (*a*) stone, including (*b*) all unusual stones, and of (*c*) all the more peculiar forms of earth. These three types of earthy substances are discussed in the order in which they occur here: less uncommon types of stone in §§ 6–7, unusual stones in §§ 8–47, and peculiar kinds of earth in §§ 48–end.

καὶ ὅσα λίθων εἴδη περιττότερα. This expression includes not only gemstones, but also many which are remarkable not so much for their appearance as for their capacity to act upon or react to other substances (§ 4), such as the lodestone (§§ 4, 29) or the touchstone (§§ 4, 46–47).

ἢ χρώμασιν. It is with reference to their use as *pigments* that Theophrastus discusses most of the earths that he discusses. See § 50, ἀλλὰ μᾶλλον ἄν τις αὐτὰς (sc. τὰς διαφοράς) τοῖς χρώμασι διαριθμήσειεν οἷσπερ καὶ οἱ γραφεῖς χρῶνται.

ἢ λειότησιν ἢ πυκνότησιν. These are notable characteristics of Samian earth (§ 62).

ἢ καὶ ἄλλη τινὶ δυνάμει. Two uses of the term δύναμις can be distinguished in the *De Lapidibus*:

1. In this passage δύναμις means no more than 'peculiar quality', a sense which it occasionally bears in Plato (*Timaeus* 82c, ἔτι δὲ ὀξείαις καὶ ἁλμυραῖς δυνάμεσι) and in Aristotle (see A. L. Peck, Aristotle, *Parts of Animals*, Introduction, p. 31, Loeb Classical Library).

Theophrastus also uses the word similarly in *C.P.* 6. 12. 2, δριμύτης ἢ καὶ ἄλλη τις τοιαύτη δύναμις: pungency is a δύναμις, just as in the present passage colour, smoothness, and density are δυνάμεις. 2. Elsewhere in the book δύναμις means 'power', 'capacity', especially the capacity to act on other substances, to react to them, or to fail to react to them (§ 4, τὰς δυνάμεις τοῦ τε ποιεῖν ἢ πάσχειν καὶ τοῦ μὴ πάσχειν). These δυνάμεις belong to stones rather than to earths and are discussed in §§ 4 and 5. Further allusions are made to them in the course of the treatise. For example, the *smaragdus* has 'certain powers' (δυνάμεις τινάς, § 23), namely the ability to communicate its colour to water, already mentioned in § 4, and its beneficial effect on the eyesight. Similarly the *lyngurium* is 'unusual in its power' (περιττὴ τῇ δυνάμει, § 28) of attracting other objects, the same being true of amber (§ 29). Many stones 'receive the power (i.e. the impact) of iron (προσδέχονται τὴν τοῦ σιδήρου δύναμιν, § 43). Finally, the touchstone has a 'power' (δύναμιν, § 45) like that of fire, because it can test the purity of gold.

περὶ μὲν οὖν τῶν μεταλλευομένων ἐν ἄλλοις τεθεώρηται. Metals were discussed in Theophrastus' lost treatise περὶ μετάλλων. Diogenes Laertius (v. 44) mentions a treatise περὶ μετάλλων in *two* books, but the evidence collected by Usener (*Analecta Theophrastea*, p. 6) suggests that the ancients knew of *one* book only. Usener is therefore justified in concluding (pp. 19–20) that Diogenes has included the περὶ λίθων twice in his catalogue, once as the second book of the περὶ μετάλλων and once as an independent work under its own title (v. 44). That Theophrastus himself regarded the περὶ μετάλλων and the περὶ λίθων as two quite independent works is shown by the phrasing of the present passage (ἐν ἄλλοις).

περὶ δὲ τούτων, sc. stones and earths.

§ 2. ἐκ καθαρᾶς τινος . . . καὶ ὁμαλῆς ὕλης. See p. 20 with n. 3.

συρροῆς, 'a conflux', a 'flowing-together'. See pp. 23–27.

διηθήσεως, 'filtering', 'straining', 'percolation'. See pp. 20–23.

εἴτε ὡς ἀνωτέρω εἴρηται, κτλ. But nothing of the kind 'has been stated above', at least in the existing text. There are similar retrospective references to missing details in §§ 50 and 61. See p. 15 with n. 2.

εἴτε . . . καὶ κατ' ἄλλον τρόπον ἐκκεκριμένης, sc. τῆς καθαρᾶς καὶ ὁμαλῆς ὕλης.

ἐκκεκριμένης, 'separated', that is, from the original earth.

τὰ μὲν . . . τὰ δ' . . . τὰ δ'. . . . ἀφ' ὧν. Theophrastus refers to the 'pure and uniform matter', or rather to individual samples of it. The phrase cannot refer to stones and earths since these are to be understood as the subject of ἔχουσι below. ἐνδέχεται, sc. συνεστάναι.

ἀφ' ὧν δὴ καὶ τὸ λεῖον, κτλ. From the 'pure and uniform matter' stones and earths derive such qualities as smoothness, solidity, lustre, and transparency. See pp. 20, 28.

ἔχουσι. The subject is the stones and earths to be discussed in the treatise.

ὅσῳ ἂν καὶ ὁμαλεστέρων καὶ καθαρωτέρων ἔκαστον ᾖ, κτλ. For the construction, cf. § 40, τὰ μέν ἐστι γῆς. . . . The purer and more uniform the matter of which each specimen (or kind) of stone or earth is composed, the more notable are the qualities (ταῦτα) of smoothness, &c. imparted to the stone or earth.

τὰ κατὰ τὴν σύστασιν ἢ πῆξιν. σύστασις, 'composition', 'formation', is immediately explained by πῆξις, 'solidification', 'hardening'. One must not be tempted into rendering this phrase as 'the *processes of* composition or solidification', for this will introduce an inconsistency. Theophrastus has just stated that certain qualities possessed by earths and stones are derived by them from the pure, uniform matter; and that furthermore such qualities correspond in their intensity to the purity and uniformity of that same matter. He would therefore be inconsistent if in summing up (τὸ . . . ὅλον) he were to suggest that the intensity of such qualities was after all due not to the perfection (ἀκρίβεια) of the pure, uniform matter, but to the perfection of the process of hardening.

The phrase ought therefore to mean 'the *matter subjected to* composition or solidification'; that is, the pure, uniform matter, which will be solidified by heat and cold into stones and earths, as is described in § 3. Rendered in this way, the sentence recapitulates the previous one, as it should: 'On the perfection of the matter subjected to composition or solidification depend the qualities derived from that matter.' The only fresh detail is the suggestion that the pure, uniform matter will be subjected to composition or solidification. The abrupt manner in which this detail is introduced is somewhat surprising, but its intrusion enables Theophrastus to pass rapidly to his next topic, solidification by heat or cold, which is briefly discussed in § 3. This brusque transition reinforces the suspicion that §§ 2 and 3 are merely a summary of a more detailed disquisition. See note on εἴτε ὡς ἀνωτέρω εἴρηται above.

For the use of κατά in τὰ κατὰ τὴν σύστασιν ἢ πῆξιν compare the force of περί in the phrase οἱ περὶ τὴν πύρωσιν καὶ καῦσιν (§ 8), 'the stones which have to do with burning and combustion'.

ἀκολουθεῖ, 'depends on'. See Arist. *Rhet.* i. 6. 3, ἀκολουθεῖ δὲ δίχως· ἢ γὰρ ἅμα ἢ ὕστερον, οἷον τῷ μὲν μανθάνειν τὸ ἐπίστασθαι ὕστερον, τῷ δὲ ὑγιαίνειν τὸ ζῆν ἅμα, and E. M. Cope's note, where the following translation is given: 'The term *attending upon* admits of two different senses, either simultaneous (attendance, accompaniment) or subsequent (consequence), as knowledge attends on learning subsequently, but life on health simultaneously.'

ἀκολουθεῖ is here used of 'consequence'. The qualities of stones and earths are in general a direct 'consequence' of the purity and uniformity of the component matter.

In § 29, however, ἀκολουθοίη is used in the other sense. The power of attraction is a simultaneous concomitant of amber, for where the one exists, the other must also exist. Cope distinguishes three other senses of ἀκολουθεῖν as a logical term. These need not be discussed here.

§ 3. ἡ δὲ πῆξις τοῖς μὲν ἀπὸ θερμοῦ τοῖς δ' ἀπὸ ψυχροῦ γίνεται, 'this solidification is due in some cases to heat and in others to cold'. But this can be true only of stones and earths taken together, since later in this section Theophrastus states that the earths all appear to be hardened by fire, that is, by heat. For a full discussion of the whole section, see pp. 28–36.

κωλύει γὰρ ἴσως οὐδὲν ἔνια γένη λίθων ὑφ' ἑκατέρων συνίστασθαι τούτων. The thought would have been easier to follow if Theophrastus had here written 'for some stones are formed by cold'. We should then have read 'This solidification is due in some cases to heat and in others to cold, for some stones are formed by cold, although it would seem that the earths are all formed by heat.' But Theophrastus appears to have been uncertain as to which stones, if any, were in fact formed by cold (see pp. 30–33). Hence the cautious remark 'for there may be nothing to prevent certain kinds of stones from being formed by either of these things', i.e. by heat or by cold.

ἐπεὶ τά γε τῆς γῆς ἅπαντα δόξειεν ἂν ὑπὸ πυρός (sc. συνίστασθαι), 'although it would seem that the earths at any rate are all formed by fire (that is, by heat), since the process whereby a thing is solidified and the process whereby it suffers disintegration belong to contrary genera.' The argument implied is the following:

1. Contrary causes have contrary effects. See the note on ἐν τοῖς ἐναντίοις below.

2. Earths are dissolved by water, that is, by cold. (Strictly speaking, they are not dissolved by water in the sense that salt is so dissolved: they are merely disintegrated. But τῆξις is used by Aristotle and Theophrastus as the antithesis of πῆξις, 'solidification', and is a more general term than the literal rendering 'dissolution' suggests.)

3. Since earths are 'dissolved' by cold, they must be solidified by that which is contrary to cold, namely by heat (that is, by fire).

With ἐν τοῖς ἐναντίοις understand γένεσι, the literal translation being 'since for each thing its solidification and its dissolution belong to contrary *genera*'. Cf. Arist. *Categ.* 14ᵃ19 ff., ἀνάγκη δὲ πάντα τὰ ἐναντία ἢ ἐν τῷ αὐτῷ γένει ἢ ἐν τοῖς ἐναντίοις γένεσιν, ἢ αὐτὰ γένη εἶναι.

Solidification (πῆξις) is a species of the genus 'coming-into-being' (γένεσις), while 'dissolution' (τῆξις) is a species of the contrary genus 'destruction' (φθορά). Now 'contrary effects are due to contrary causes' (τὰ ἐναντία τῶν ἐναντίων αἴτια, Arist. *Mete.* 384ᵇ2–3). Consequently, if the dissolution of earths is caused by *cold* (that is, by water), their solidification or hardening must be caused by *heat* (that is, by fire).

ἰδιότητες δὲ . . . αἱ πολλαὶ διαφοραί. Theophrastus uses ἰδιότητες ('peculiarities') and διαφοραί ('differences') as if they were virtually equivalent terms, ignoring the logical distinction between an ἴδιον ('property') and a διαφορά ('differentia'). We may compare *H.P.* 3. 2. 6, αἱ γὰρ διαφοραὶ τῆς χώρας τὴν ἰδιότητα ποιοῦσιν. ἀλλ' εἴρηται τὸ ἴδιον ὡς ἐπὶ πᾶν ('the word "peculiar" is used in a general sense').

αἱ πολλαὶ διαφοραί. See the critical apparatus. For the construction, cf. *H.P.* 1. 10. 8, ἁπλῶς δὲ αἱ διαφοραὶ τῶν φύλλων ἢ μεγέθει ἢ πλήθει, κτλ. This emendation is further supported by the fact that διαφοραί must be understood in the next sentence with αἱ κατὰ τὰς δυνάμεις. For this, if for no other reason, the reading αἱ ῥοαὶ διάφοροι proposed by Furlanus and adopted by Hill is impossible.

§ 4. τοῖς δὲ λίθοις . . . τοῦ μὴ πάσχειν. Both earths and stones possess distinctive characteristics (διαφοραί) in respect of colour, smoothness, solidity, and the like (§ 3 *fin.*). But besides such characteristics, *stones* have others which have to do with their capacity (*a*) to act on other substances (ποιεῖν), (*b*) to react to other substances (πάσχειν), and (*c*) to fail to react to other substances (μὴ πάσχειν). See also the note on δύναμις in § 1.

In §§ 4 and 5 Theophrastus illustrates this statement. As instances of (*a*) acting on other substances, he mentions the power attributed to the *smaragdus* of imparting a green hue to water, the petrifying action possessed by certain stones not specified, the power of attraction exercised by the lodestone, and the touchstone's power of testing metals.

As instances of (*b*) reacting to other substances, he refers to fusibility (τηκτοί), combustibility (καυστοί), and the capacity to be carved (γλυπτοί), turned on a lathe (τορνευτοί), or sawn (πριστοί).

As instances of (*c*) the failure to react, he refers to infusibility (ἄτηκτοι), incombustibility (ἄκαυστοι), and inability to be worked (τῶν δὲ οὐδὲ ὅλως ἅπτεται σιδήριον, κτλ.).

τηκτοὶ γὰρ οἱ δ' ἄτηκτοι. For the idiom, cf. Arist. *Poetics* 1447ᵇ14, ἐλεγειοποιοὺς τοὺς δὲ ἐποποιοὺς ὀνομάζουσιν.

Theophrastus begins by citing examples of the capacity to react or to fail to react. There follow (§ 4, ἔνιοι δὲ κτλ.) instances of the capacity to act on other substances, whereupon Theophrastus returns (§ 5, γνωριμωτέρα δὲ κτλ.) to examples of the former categories. τηκτοὶ γὰρ. In § 9 slag, millstones, and *pyromachi* are stated to be fusible.

οἱ δ' ἄτηκτοι. For Theophrastus the majority of stones would count as infusible since it was impossible with the methods then known to obtain temperatures high enough to fuse them. οἱ δ' ἄκαυστοι. Theophrastus mentions several instances of incombustible stones in §§ 18–19.

καὶ ἐν αὐτῇ τῇ καύσει καὶ πυρώσει πλείους ἔχοντες διαφοράς. Theophrastus is not content merely to say that some stones are combustible (καυστοί). Their reaction to fire may take several forms, as he shows in §§ 10–17. For the distinction between καῦσις and πύρωσις see the note on § 8.

οἱ δ' ὅλως ἀπολιθοῦν τὰ τιθέμενα εἰς ἑαυτούς. No further allusion is made to this topic in the *De Lapidibus*, but it was no doubt included in the lost monograph 'On Petrifactions' (περὶ τῶν ἀπολιθουμένων, Diog. Laert. v. 42). See § 38 and note. The stone in question was used for coffins. Cf. *De Igne*, 46 (where ἐν Λυκίᾳ should probably be read for ἐν κύκλῳ) and Pliny xxxvi. 131. See p. 34, n. 1.

ἕτεροι δ' ὁλκήν τινα ποιεῖν. Cf. §§ 28–29, where the *lyngurium*, amber, and the lodestone are cited as stones possessing a power of attraction.

οἱ δὲ βασανίζειν, κτλ. The appearance and action of the touchstone are described in §§ 45–47.

τὸν χρυσὸν καὶ τὸν ἄργυρον. No other classical writer suggests that the touchstone can be used for testing *silver* as well as gold. Theophrastus is, however, quite correct. See C. G. E. Bunt, '*Chaffers' Handbook to Hall Marks on Gold and Silver Plate*, 7th edition, 1945, pp. 4–5.

ὥσπερ ἥ τε . . . καὶ ἡ Λυδή. In this phrase ἥ τε καλουμένη λίθος 'Ηρακλεία refers to ἕτεροι δ' ὁλκήν τινα ποιεῖν and is the lodestone. Cf. Plato, *Ion* 533d, ὥσπερ ἐν τῇ λίθῳ ἣν Εὐριπίδης μὲν Μαγνῆτιν ὠνόμασεν, οἱ δὲ πολλοὶ 'Ηρακλείαν. Only ἡ Λυδή refers to οἱ δὲ βασανίζειν, this being the touchstone, which was found in a Lydian river (see § 47 and note).

§ 5. ἡ τῶν τικτόντων. These are stones which rattle when shaken and were therefore thought to be pregnant. Later they were known as *aëtitae*, eagle-stones (Pliny xxxvi. 149–51). The commonest are limonite nodules with a detached core.

With ⟨ἡ⟩ κατὰ τὰς ἐργασίας understand διαφορά. Cf. § 41, ὅλως μὲν ἡ κατὰ τὰς ἐργασίας . . . πολλὴ διαφορά.

γλυπτοὶ γὰρ ἔνιοι καὶ τορνευτοὶ καὶ πριστοί See § 42, where Theophrastus points out that many stones can be worked by *all* the recognized methods.

εἰσὶ δὲ πλείους καὶ ἄλλαι κατὰ ταύτας ⟨διαφοραί⟩. κατὰ ταύτας, sc. τὰς ἐργασίας. Other methods of working stones are hinted at in § 43.

§ 6. In this section Theophrastus refers to the marbles of Paros, Pentelicus, and Chios, and to the granite of Syene (Aswan). *Alabastrites* is onyx marble (oriental alabaster), and so probably is *chernites*, which is 'like ivory'. The Darius mentioned is probably Darius III, who is referred to simply as 'Darius' in *H.P.* 2. 2. 7. The details of his burial, carried out under Alexander's instructions (Arrian, *Anabasis*, iii. 22. 1), would be widely discussed.

§ 7. καὶ ὁ πόρος ὅμοιος τῷ χρώματι καὶ τῇ πυκνότητι τῷ Παρίῳ τὴν δὲ κουφότητα μόνον ἔχων τοῦ πόρου. Liddell and Scott⁹, s.v. πῶρος, take this statement to be a *general* description of poros-stone. This is also the view of J. Frazer, *Pausanias' Description of Greece*, vol. iii, pp. 502–3, and S. Casson, *Technique of Early Greek Sculpture*, pp. 72–73. But it is hardly credible that Theophrastus would describe poros in general as 'being similar to Parian stone in colour and solidity, and possessing merely the lightness of poros', that is, of itself. The last remark would be pointless. It may be noted that authorities habitually slur over the remark 'and possessing merely the lightness of poros'. Liddell and Scott write 'but lighter', Frazer writes 'but not so heavy', Pliny (xxxvi. 132) 'minus tantum ponderosus'.

The words καὶ ὁ πόρος must refer to a *special* variety of poros found in Egypt and used, as Theophrastus himself tells us, in fine buildings. As such, it is tacitly contrasted with the poros of Greece, which was indeed used in fine buildings, particularly in temples, but was at the same time the common building-stone of the country.

Thus, to state that this special variety combined the colour and density of Parian marble with the lightness of (ordinary) poros would be reasonable since the ordinary variety would be familiar to most of Theophrastus' readers. The phrase καὶ ὁ πόρος κτλ. is admittedly ambiguous, but the ambiguity disappears when the sentence is considered in conjunction with the surrounding context. The preceding sentence contains a reference to two stones, *alabastrites* and *chernites*, one of which, the *alabastrites*, is *stated* to be *Egyptian*. The sentence which follows similarly refers to an *Egyptian* stone ('a black, transparent stone found there', i.e. in Egypt, the last place to be mentioned).

Consequently καὶ ὁ πόρος κτλ. must mean *Egyptian* poros. For if it refers to poros in general, the sequence of the whole passage is broken. See *Classical Review*, lviii (1944), 18.

διάζωμα. The meaning of this word is elusive. Hill translates 'partitions', while Schneider and Wimmer merely transliterate into 'diazoma'. Liddell and Scott⁹ assume that it means 'frieze', 'cornice', like διάζωσμα in Athenaeus v. 205c, where it is applied to the carved frieze in the main cabin of Ptolemy Philopator's state barge. 'Frieze' is the rendering of Caley and Richards.

Turnebus, whose rendering is 'cingulis distinguunt', seems to come nearest to the truth. 'Cingulae' means 'bands'. Athenaeus, in a passage (v. 206c) possibly known to Turnebus, writes καὶ τοὺς τοίχους δὲ λευκαῖς καὶ μελαίναις διαποικίλλουσι πλινθίσιν, ἐνίοτε δὲ καὶ τοῖς ἀπὸ τῆς ἀλαβαστίτιδος προσαγορευομένης πέτρας, that is, 'They (the Egyptians) diversify their walls too with white and black courses of stones, and sometimes also with blocks of the stone known as *alabastitis*' (onyx marble). The black and white stones are no doubt the dark granite from Syene and the white limestone which is to be identified with Theophrastus' poros. Both kinds of stone were widely used in important buildings. It seems probable that Theophrastus is alluding to the Egyptian practice of using bands or rather courses of poros so as to contrast decoratively with similar courses of black granite. Hence 'course' seems to be the meaning of διάζωμα in this passage.

καὶ μέλας, κτλ. The 'black, transparent stone' is perhaps freshly quarried basalt.

αἱ δὲ κατὰ τὰς δυνάμεις τὰς προειρημένας, κτλ. The 'capacities previously mentioned' are those discussed in §§ 3–5, for example the power of attraction. As opposed to qualities of colour, hardness, softness, smoothness, &c., such capacities are uncommon.

οὐκέτι τόποις ὅλοις . . . μεγέθεσιν. For οὐκέτι meaning *non item*, cf. Theophr., *De Sensu et Sensibilibus*, § 36, τοῦτο δὲ οὐκέτι συνεῖδον, and E. M. Cope's edition of Aristotle, *Rhetoric*, vol. i, p. 14. Such capacities, unlike the commoner qualities, do not belong to stones (*a*) of a whole region (τόποις ὅλοις) or (*b*) occurring in continuous masses (συνεχείαις λίθων) or (*c*) of great size (μεγέθεσιν). These three points are taken up in § 8. Some of the stones endowed with these capacities are (*a*) quite rare (σπάνιοι πάμπαν) and (*c*) small (σμικροί), and some (*b*) are actually found enclosed in other stones when these are split in two (οἱ δὲ καὶ ἐν ἑτέροις εὑρίσκονται διακοπτομένοις).

§ 8. For the *smaragdus* (in Theophrastus probably never the emerald), see §§ 4, 23–27, 35; for the 'sard', see § 30; for the *anthrax*, see §§ 18–19; for the *sapphirus* (lapis lazuli), see §§ 23, 37. One δύναμις of the *smaragdus* has been mentioned in § 4. But here Theophrastus is probably more concerned with a δύναμις possessed by most of the stones used as signets, namely that of resisting iron tools: see § 41 and the note.

καὶ σχεδὸν οἱ ἐν λόγῳ τῶν εἰς τὰ σφραγίδια γλυπτῶν. See the critical apparatus. For this use of ἐν λόγῳ cf. *C.P.* 6. 12. 7, τὰ δὲ ἄλλα ὡς ἂν ἐν φαρμακοῦ λόγῳ, 'the rest may count as drugs'.

οἱ δὲ καὶ ἐν ἑτέροις εὑρίσκονται διακοπτομένοις. As instances of stones found enclosed in other stones Theophrastus cites the Lipara stones (§ 14), Melian pumice (§§ 14, 21), and rock-crystal, amethyst, and 'sard' (§ 30).

ὀλίγοι δὲ καὶ οἱ περὶ τὴν πύρωσιν καὶ καῦσιν, that is, stones notable for their δυνάμεις in reacting to fire are few. Such stones are discussed below in §§ 9–19. καῦσις, a more restricted term than πύρωσις, means 'combustion', 'reduction to ashes'. Cf. Arist. *Mete.* 387ᵇ13–14, καυστὰ δὲ δοκεῖ εἶναι ὅσα εἰς τέφραν διαλύεται τῶν σωμάτων. On the other hand πύρωσις, 'exposure to fire', applies not only to combustible, but also to fusible substances. See § 9, κατὰ δὴ τὴν πύρωσιν οἱ μὲν τήκονται. It connotes in fact almost any process of heating by fire, even cooking. Cf. *H.P.* 7. 7. 2, ἔνια γὰρ δεῖται πυρώσεως, ὥσπερ μαλάχη, κτλ.

CHAPTER II

§ 9. ῥεῖ γὰρ . . . ἡ λίθος ἡ ἐκ τούτων. 'The stone from them' is clearly slag formed in the process of reducing metals from their ores. See pp. 30–31.

δι' αὐτούς. See the critical apparatus. Wimmer, following earlier editors, translates 'suapte natura', and is followed apparently by Caley and Richards. But there is no sense in saying that the slag melts owing to the moisture of its constituents or *because of its own nature*. Moreover, αὐτούς cannot refer to the slag, ἡ λίθος. It can only refer to the metals just mentioned, silver, copper, and iron. The slag melts either owing to the moisture of its constituents or *because of the (presence of the) metals*, which are themselves formed from moist matter (§ 1), and are therefore apt to be fused.

καὶ οἱ πυρομάχοι καὶ οἱ μυλίαι. Caley and Richards (op. cit., p. 77) argue that these stones were fluxes. The descriptions, however, given in the *Meteorologica* (see p. 31) and by Theophrastus suggest rather that they were the building materials of lime kilns and the hearths of iron furnaces, where they were *subjected to* a fluxing agent (lime), 'the material heaped upon them'. *Pyromachi* were probably refractory siliceous rock, and the millstones acidic lavas.

συρρέουσιν οἷς. The manuscripts read ῥέουσιν οἷς, for which Schneider proposed ῥέουσιν σὺν οἷς, but σὺν οἷς is not good Attic Greek. The conjecture of Caley and Richards restores the sense and the grammar, and the correction is similar to that of § 2, where with Schneider and Wimmer they rightly read συρροῆς for ῥοῆς.

οἱ δὲ ... λέγουσι. Neither here nor in § 28, οἱ δέ φασιν, does οἱ μέν or ἔνιοι precede. H.P. 4. 5. 3, οἱ δὲ ... φασιν, is another instance, so that no emendation is necessary.

μάρμαρος, as is shown by the reference to quicklime in the next sentence, here means 'limestone' in general, including probably crystalline limestone (marble). The word is not used specifically of marble until a later date.

κονία is used in two senses in the course of this work. Here and in §§ 68 and 69 it means 'quicklime', but in § 40 a fine powder. Both uses are well attested: see Liddell and Scott⁹, s.v., and also pp. 44–47. The people who asserted that 'all stones melt with the exception of limestone, which is calcined and turns into lime' were probably not philosophers, none of whom is known to have held such a view. It is more likely that they were craftsmen drawing upon their own experience, and in particular the smelters and lime-burners who carried out the processes mentioned earlier in this section.

§ 10. πολλοὶ γὰρ ... τὴν πύρωσιν. Theophrastus may still have limestone in mind. At least one instance is known of a limestone which could not be burnt in a particular kiln because it broke and flew into pieces (R. H. S. Robertson in a letter, 5 September 1960).

ὥσπερ οὐδ' ὁ κέραμος. For the resistance of potters' clay to fire, see Arist. Mete. 384ᵃ20 ff., where it is attributed to the elimination of the moisture brought about by the process of firing in the ovens. Theophrastus similarly attributes the resistance of some stones to fire to the loss of the moisture originally contained in them (ἐξυγρασμένοι).

τὸ γὰρ τηκτὸν ἔνικμον εἶναι δεῖ. This remark is meant to apply only to substances which are to be melted by *fire*. It does not include things that are soluble in water. For instance, salt and natron are soluble in water, but contain no water in their natural state (Arist. Mete. 383ᵇ13, 385ᵇ8–9).

§ 11. ἀχρείους. Useless for what? Caley and Richards (op. cit., p. 79) suggest 'for cutting and carving', and cite sandstone as an instance. But for cutting and carving the second group of stones mentioned in this sentence, those that become softer and 'more friable' (διαθραύστους μᾶλλον, which is loosely rendered by Caley and Richards 'are more easily broken'), would be equally useless, whereas, if anything, the contrary is implied by Theophrastus. He must still be referring to stones that are to be broken up for burning. Large, very dry lumps of limestone would not burn.

ἀμφοτέρων μὲν ἐξαιρεῖται τὴν ὑγρότητα. A difficult sentence. Schneider suggests that ὁ ἥλιος should be understood from ἡλιουμένων. θραυστοὺς ... καὶ κατακτούς. See the critical apparatus. The usual reading θραυστοὺς ... καὶ τηκτούς is open to objection. To assert that loss of moisture makes these, or indeed any stones, liable to melt is a contradiction of the principle stated in § 10, that a thing which is capable of being melted must contain moisture. Hence in the present text καὶ κατακτούς is read for καὶ τηκτούς. The terms θραυστός and κατακτός are similarly associated in Arist. *Mete.* 386ᵃ11, where they are applied to pottery (κέραμος δὲ καὶ θραυστὸν καὶ κατακτόν) and in Arist. *H.A.* 523ᵇ10 ff., where they are used of oyster-shells and other hard shells. The distinction between the two terms is explained in Arist. *Mete.* 386ᵃ9 ff. Fragility (κατάξις) involves a division into large parts, friability (θραῦσις) a division into small parts, more than two in number.

§§ 12–13. In these paragraphs Theophrastus describes two stones which are found in the same part of Thrace.

Of the first, the stone of Binae, he writes that:

1. It is carried down by a river.
2. It burns when charcoal is heaped upon it.
3. It burns only so long as it is fanned.
4. It has an offensive smell.

In describing the second, *spinos*, he mentions that:

(a) It burns when it is split up and placed in the sun.
(b) It burns more fiercely when it is sprinkled with water.

In [Aristotle] *De Mir. Aus.* 841ᵃ21 ff., chap. 115, there is a description of a stone which appears to combine in itself some of the characteristics of the Binae stone and of *spinos*. Like the Binae stone, it is carried down by a Thracian river and has an offensive smell; like *spinos*, it burns more fiercely when it is sprinkled with water. This information appears to have been derived from the fourth-century historian Theopompus (see V. Rose, *Aristoteles Pseudepigraphus*, p. 255). It is therefore likely that Theophrastus is here correcting the misapprehensions of Theopompus, as O. Regenbogen has suggested (Pauly–Wissowa, s.v. Theophrastus, Suppl.-Band VII, Cols. 1407–8). It is by no means surprising that Theopompus confused the two stones since they are closely akin. Both are varieties of lignite.

§ 12. The meaning of ἀνθρακοῦνται in this passage is open to dispute. Liddell and Scott⁹ translate ἀνθρακοῦσθαι 'to be burnt to cinders or ashes', which is the sense required in Aeschylus, *Prometheus Vinctus*, 372. In the present passage Hill's rendering is 'become like burning coals' (by 'coals' he means 'charcoal'), and Wimmer's likewise is 'abeunt in carbones'. There is no reason why the word should not bear either sense, but the second, which is incidentally the more literal of the two, is clearly demanded here. For Theophrastus adds that the stones which ἀνθρακοῦνται 'last a long time'; and this can hardly be the case if the immediate effect of combustion is to reduce them to ashes. On the other hand, if they 'glow like charcoal', they will naturally be expected to burn for some time.

περὶ Βίνας. Binae appears to have been a settlement in Thrace on the river Pontus (mod. Strumitza), a tributary of the Strymon (Struma).

καὶ μέχρι τούτου ἄχρις ἂν φυσᾷ τις. The present subjunctive shows that 'so long as', not 'until', is the meaning. The manuscript readings do not justify the substitution of φυσήσῃ for φυσᾷ.

According to Theophrastus, then, these stones from Binae continue to burn so long as they are fanned. Here we have further confirmation that he is criticizing and correcting the information given in [Aristotle] *De Mir. Aus.* 841ᵃ, chap. 115 (see the earlier note on §§ 12–13), where the stones, so far from burning so long as they are fanned, are said to be extinguished as soon as they are fanned (ῥιπιζόμενοι γὰρ σβέννυνται τάχεως).

Probably Theophrastus is right. He has already stated that the stones require the addition of charcoal to make them burn, and this suggests that their combustibility was low. Now even charcoal needs a forced draught if it is to burn properly, as Theophrastus knew (*De Igne* 28, ὁ δ᾿ ἄνθραξ καὶ τὸ ξύλον οὐ δύναται καίεσθαι μὴ φυσώμενα, and still more would this be the case with a mixture consisting of charcoal and these stones.

For μέχρι τούτου used as the correlative of 'so long as' cf. Aristotle, *Mete.* 355ᵃ3–4, καὶ γὰρ τὸ φανερὸν πῦρ, ἕως ἂν ἔχῃ τροφήν, μέχρι τούτου ζῆν, and Andocides, *De Mysteriis*, 69.

§ 13. *Spinos* was perhaps more shaly and pyritous than the other varieties of lignite mentioned by Theophrastus.

§ 14. ἐκπορῦται. Here and at the beginning of § 15 the manuscripts and most editions have ἐκφορῦται, a word which cannot be linked with any of the meanings of φόρος, φορά, ἔκφορος or ἐκφορά. Liddell and Scott⁹ give the rendering 'to be worn into holes', presumably following Wimmer's translation 'exinanitur', which can ultimately be traced to that of Turnebus. But there can be little doubt that Turnebus meant to recommend by his translation the reading ἐκπορούται, 'is filled with πόροι, passages'. (He was in the habit of using his translation to suggest emendations which do not appear in his text.) This reading is adopted in the present text. Theophrastus likes compound verbs of this type. Usually they mean 'be turned into . . .', e.g. ἐκσαρκοῦσθαι, ἐκξυλοῦσθαι. But ἐκζωοῦσθαι, 'be filled with worms' (C.P. 4. 8. 4), has exactly the force required for ἐκπορούσθαι, 'be filled with passages', 'be worn into passages'.

Hill, following de Laet and Salmasius reads ἐκπωροῦται, which should mean 'is reduced to poros-stone'. But the Lipara stone could hardly become both like poros-stone (see p. 92) and like pumice. The Lipara stone is probably not obsidian, but pitchstone; see R. H. S. Robertson, Classical Review, N.S., xiii (1963), 132.

ὥσθ' ἅμα τήν τε χρόαν μεταβάλλειν . . . μέλας τε γὰρ . . . ἄκαυστος ὤν. The change of colour from black to grey would in Theophrastus' opinion be due to the loss of moisture. See De Igne 39, οὐδὲν γὰρ μέλαν ἄνευ ὑγρότητος.

ἐν τῇ κισσήρει. Apart from κίτηρις, which occurs once in § 19, κίσσηρις is the form found in the manuscripts here and in §§ 19–22. According to Aspasius, Commentaria in Aristotelem Graeca, vol. xix, pt. 1, p. 65. 4, the correct form is κίσηρις.

καὶ εἴη ἂν τούτω ὥσπερ ἀντιπεπονθώς· πλὴν ὁ λίθος οὗτος οὐχ ὅμοιος τῷ Λιπαραίῳ. See the critical apparatus. Wimmer (reading ἐκεῖνος μὲν) translates 'Hic igitur illi quasi contrario modo nascitur . . .', an unconvincing rendering. Schneider suggests for ἀντιπεπονθώς 'naturae et qualitatis contrariae' and is apparently followed by Liddell and Scott[9], s.v. ἀντιπάσχω, where 'to be of opposite nature to' is given as the meaning of the word in this passage, but in this passage alone. This sense is not only unusual, but unsuitable, since it takes no account of the next phrase, πλὴν ὁ λίθος οὗτος, κτλ. To say that the Lipara stone 'is of opposite nature to the other, except that this other is not like the Lipara stone' is nonsense.

Better sense is given if ἀντιπεπονθώς is assumed to mean 'suffering the opposite of'. But again the phrase πλὴν ὁ λίθος οὗτος κτλ. is a stumbling-block. Why should Theophrastus write that the Lipara stone 'will prove to have suffered the opposite of the other stone', and then add 'except that this stone is not like the Lipara stone'?

ἀντιπάσχειν bears another meaning akin to 'suffer the opposite of', namely 'to be reciprocally (or rather, inversely) proportional to'. See Liddell and Scott[9], s.v. If εἴη ἂν ἀντιπεπονθώς is here rendered 'will be inversely proportional to', 'will stand in an inverse relationship to', no difficulty is offered by the phrase πλὴν ὁ λίθος οὗτος κτλ. The Lipara stone 'will stand in an inverse relationship to the Melian stone, except that this latter is not like the Lipara stone'. Theophrastus has a mathematical idea in his mind.

Three sets of stones are involved: (1) the Lipara stone, the subject of the main clause, which we may call A; (2) the Melian stone (τούτῳ, ὁ λίθος οὗτος), just mentioned (A'); and (3) two lots of pumice (P), that of Lipara, and that of Melos.

Now the Lipara stone is contained by pumice; the Melian stone contains pumice. A is contained by P while A' contains P. Thus A 'suffers the opposite of' (ἀντιπάσχει) or, more precisely, is inversely related to A'. In other words

$$A:P = P:A'.$$

Only (πλὴν ὁ λίθος οὗτος οὐχ ὅμοιος), A and A' are not identical. Consequently there is no proper equation, and the inverse relationship is no more than approximate. Why Theophrastus should have chosen to labour a simple point in this way is not at all clear. Possibly it was a lecture-room joke.

The rendering of Caley and Richards, 'corresponds to this in the opposite way', approaches the required sense more closely than other versions, but needs elucidating.

This Melian stone, dissimilar to that of Lipara (pitchstone) although similarly found with pumice, must be obsidian.

§ 15. The reading ὁ δὲ λίθος ⟨ὁ⟩ κτλ. is necessary because otherwise ὁ δὲ λίθος will refer back to the stone of Tetras, which will thus be identical with that of Cape Erineas. The descriptions show that they were not identical. The former was presumably pitchstone from Lipara that had been washed up on the north coast of Sicily. The latter may be asphalt from south-east Sicily (H. Michell, *The Economics of Ancient Greece*, p. 114). Neither place has been identified. *16/152*

§ 16. Lignite is mined in Elis at Brouma, which has been identified with the ancient Salmone.

§ 17. ἐν τοῖς ἐν Σκαπτῇ Ὕλῃ μετάλλοις. See the critical apparatus, and for the construction cf. § 63, ἐν τοῖς ἐν Σάμῳ sc. γεωφανέσιν. The possessive genitive of the usual reading, ἐν τοῖς Σκαπτησύλης μετάλλοις is not normal with places. Note that in § 6 Theophrastus writes, as would be expected, not Πάρου, Πεντελικοῦ, but Παρίων, Πεντελικῶν. Scaptehyle lay near the frontier of Thrace and Macedonia between the rivers Strymon and Nestus. The stone was probably the asbestiform mineral palygorskite; see R. H. S. Robertson, *Classical Review*, N.S., xiii (1963), 132.

CHAPTER III

§ 18. ὥσπερ ἐξ ἐναντίων πεφυκός, that is, as though composed of materials opposite in their nature to those of coal, which bears the same name (ἄνθραξ). Other writers also draw attention to the fireproof qualities of the ἄνθραξ, notably Aristotle (*Mete.* 387ᵇ17–18) and Pliny (xxxvii. 92). They may have been confusing the red garnet with the ruby. The latter is incombustible, the former is not.

τεττεράκοντα χρυσῶν, that is, forty gold staters or Darics. With χρυσῶν (from χρυσοῦς) understand στατήρων. See Liddell and Scott⁹, s.v. χρύσεος.

ἐκ Καρχηδόνος καὶ Μασσαλίας. The Carthaginian red garnets seem to have come from a region lying south-west of the Fezzan Oasis (Pliny v. 34, 35–37). Marseilles was presumably supplied from Celtic sources: pyrope could have reached it from the Vosges or Bohemia, and almandine from the Tyrol and south Germany.

§ 19. ὁ περὶ Μίλητον. This was red garnet from the neighbourhood of Alabanda, some 50 miles east of Miletus.

ὃ καὶ θαυμαστόν ἐστιν. Editors take this phrase with what precedes it, namely καλοῦσι δ' ἄνθρακα καὶ τοῦτον. In this case, we are to conclude that 'anthrax' is a strange name for the Milesian stone because in some respects 'adamas' is similar to it. But this fact would not constitute any sort of valid objection to the name 'anthrax', which is quite appropriate to the Milesian stone. Theophrastus states that the 'anthrax' discussed in § 18 received its name because in a strong light it would glow like an ember, and he could not have been surprised if the same name was applied to this Milesian 'anthrax' provided that he knew its colour. And this he probably did know, seeing that he knew something of the structure of the stone.

Reasonable sense is yielded if we change the punctuation, treat ὅμοιον γὰρ τρόπον τινὰ καὶ τὸ τοῦ ἀδάμαντος as a parenthesis, and take ὃ καὶ θαυμαστόν ἐστιν with the sentence which follows the former, οὐ γὰρ οὐδ' ὥσπερ κτλ. The whole passage then runs as follows: 'This too is called "anthrax". What is also surprising (and incidentally the properties of the "adamas" are in a manner similar) is that it does not seem in any way to be the absence of moisture that makes the "anthrax" incombustible. . . .' Thus the strange fact to which Theophrastus wishes to draw our attention is the unusual cause of the incombustibility of the 'anthrax'. With the sequence ὃ καὶ θαυμαστόν ἐστιν . . . οὐ γὰρ οὐδ' κτλ. we may compare [Aristotle] *De Mir. Aus.* 841ᵇ 24–25, ὃ δὲ πάντων ἄν τις μάλιστα θαυμάσειεν· οἱ μὲν γὰρ ἱέρακες κτλ. Cf. J. D. Denniston, *The Greek Particles*, p. 60. Somewhat similar is

Demosthenes, *Aristogeiton* I, 31, ὃ καὶ θαυμαστόν ἐστιν, εἴ τις ... ἀγνοεῖ, where εἰ, like γάρ above, is, strictly speaking, superfluous. οὐ γὰρ οὐδ᾽ ὥσπερ. Cf. *C.P.* 2. 6. 2, οὐδὲ γὰρ οὐδ᾽ ὅμοια. δόξειεν ἄν, sc. μὴ καίεσθαι to be supplied from οὐ καίεται at the beginning of this section. διὰ τὸ μηδὲν ἔχειν ὑγρόν. Unlike the 'anthrax' and the 'adamas', pumice and cinders are incombustible because they contain no moisture. For this idea, see Aristotle, loc. cit., below. Theophrastus, however, does not explain why the 'anthrax' and the 'adamas' are incombustible. Aristotle (*Mete.* 387ª17 ff.) suggests two causes of incombustibility, apart from the absence of moisture: (*a*) excess of moisture, and (*b*) absence of pores that admit fire. There is no means of deciding which of these two explanations Theophrastus accepted in the present case, but the second, or something like it, is that which he probably has in mind. His successor, Strato, attributed both the incombustibility and the recalcitrance of the 'adamas' to its πυκνότης (density). See F. Wehrli, *Straton von Lampsakos* (Die Schule des Aristoteles, vol. v), Basle, 1950, frag. 56.

The ἀδάμας of the present passage is almost certainly not a diamond.

πλὴν τῆς ἐκ τοῦ ἀφροῦ τῆς θαλάσσης συνισταμένης. There is an explanation of the way in which pumice is supposed to be formed from sea-foam in [Arist.] *De Plantis* 823ᵇ.

§ 20. ἐν τοῖς ⟨καιομένοις⟩ μάλιστα. Schneider's reconstruction of the text is satisfactory. For καιόμενος in the sense of 'volcanic', cf. [Arist.] *De Mir. Aus.* 842ᵇ20–21, ὁ δὲ καιόμενος τόπος ἐστὶν οὐ πολύς.

§ 21. καὶ πλείους τρόποι τῆς γενέσεως. Three explanations are suggested in the course of the discussion: some pumice is formed from sea-foam, some by volcanic action, and some from sand.

Schneider's emendation ἀπαμήσωνται, 'when they scrape away the top-soil', gives good sense. ἀπαμᾶν normally means 'to cut off', but since ἐπαμᾶσθαι is used in § 28 in the sense of 'scrape over', the analogous use of ἀπαμᾶσθαι in this passage is not improbable. Cf. Thuc. iv. 26, διαμώμενοι τὸν κάχληκα, 'scraping through the shingle'.

πᾶσα μὲν ⟨βαρεῖα⟩. It is clear from ἡ δ᾽ αὖ that the missing word must contrast with what precedes. βαρεῖα is suggested as the obvious antithesis to ἐλαφρά. Pliny (xxxvi. 154) mentions Melos and Nisyros, together with the Aeolian Islands, as sources of the best pumice.

καθάπερ ἐλέχθη πρότερον. See § 14.

§ 22. ἐκ τοῦ ῥύακος. Theophrastus wrote a monograph 'On the Sicilian Lava-flow' (περὶ ῥύακος τοῦ ἐν Σικελίᾳ, Diog. Laert. v. 49).

αὕτη γε καὶ μυλώδης. See the critical apparatus. For the phrasing, as thus emended, cf. *C.P.* 4. 4. 2, ἀλλ᾽ ἴσως τοῦτό γε καὶ ἀναγκαῖον.

ἀφ᾽ ὧν καὶ εἰς τοῦτο ἐξέβημεν. The description of combustible and fire-proof stones began in § 9. From this topic Theophrastus digressed to pumice in § 19.

ἐν ἄλλοις θεωρητέον τὰς αἰτίας. The causes of combustibility and incombustibility in stones are nowhere treated formally in the extant works of Theophrastus. Such a discussion might well have been included in the *De Igne*, but this work contains only passing references to stones. See, for instance, § 35.

CHAPTER IV

§ 23. ⟨περιτταὶ⟩ is preferable to Wimmer's ⟨διάφοροι⟩, a word which gives good sense, but occurs only once elsewhere (§ 50) in the *De Lapidibus*. περιττός is comparatively frequent (§§ 6, 28, 34, 36, 41, and 49). ἴασπις. See § 27 and note.

ὥσπερ χρυσόπαστος. Particles of pyrites resembling gold in colour and lustre are often enclosed in lapis lazuli *(sapphirus)*. ὥσπερ εἴπομεν. See § 4. No stone has this property.

§ 24. καὶ πρὸς τὰ ὄμματα ἀγαθή. Green is a restful colour, and green stones may have been favoured for this reason (see Pliny xxxvii. 62–63).

ταῖς ἀναγραφαῖς . . . ὑπὲρ τῶν βασιλέων τῶν Αἰγυπτίων. These records are mentioned on several occasions by Diodorus Siculus, who, like Theophrastus, claims to have made use of them (1. 69. 7). τετράπηχυν. There were two kinds of Egyptian cubit, the 'royal' of approximately 21 inches and a smaller one of about 18 inches. See How and Wells, *A Commentary on Herodotus*, vol. i, p. 138. Presumably the royal cubit is the basis of the measurements quoted in this section.

ἐν τῷ τοῦ Διός. Greek writers identified the Egyptian god Amon with Zeus (Herodotus ii. 42: see How and Wells, vol. i, p. 186). Two seats of Amon worship were well known to the Greeks, the temple and oracle of Zeus Ammon at the Siwa Oasis in the Libyan Desert and the temple and parent oracle at Thebes (Karnak). See Herodotus ii. 55 and 143. There is nothing in the text to show which of the two temples is referred to here, but the available evidence is entirely in favour of the temple at Thebes. No obelisks are known to have been erected in the Siwa Oasis, and it is unlikely that any large ones were ever transported to a site which could only be reached by a difficult land-route. All the obelisks known to us were originally erected at places adjacent to the Nile and accomplished the major part of their journey by water (see H. H. Gorringe, *Egyptian Obelisks*, pp. 119 ff.). It may also be noted that when Theophrastus refers elsewhere to the Siwa Oasis, he uses the term 'Ammon' (*H.P.* 4. 3. 5, ἐν Ἄμμωνος, and 5. 3. 7, παρ' Ἄμμωνι).

No obelisks of *green* stone have been found at Thebes or in any other part of Egypt, with the exception of two small obelisks of dark-green basalt, the fragments of which are now in the British Museum (Gorringe, op. cit., p. 138). These, along with the sandstone obelisks of Philae, are, so far as is known, the only examples not constructed of red granite ('syenite', Gorringe, loc. cit.).

ὀβελίσκους σμαράγδου τέτταρας, the reading of Salmasius, gives satisfactory sense and is close to that of the manuscripts, ὀβελίσκους σμαράγδους τέτταρας.

Other readings are open to serious objections. Wimmer, following Aldus, reads ἀνακεῖσθαι δὲ καὶ ἐν τῷ τοῦ Διὸς ὀβελίσκῳ σμαράγδους τέτταρας ('in obelisco Jovis quatuor esse smaragdos'). It is difficult to imagine how four stones, each measuring $40 \times 4 \times 2$ cubits, were arranged on one obelisk. The rendering of Caley and Richards, 'four such stones are deposited as an offering in the obelisk of Zeus', raises a similar difficulty.

Pliny, in a passage (xxxvii. 74) based on the present statement, writes: 'et fuisse apud eos in Iouis delubro obeliscum e quattuor smaragdis'; and on the strength of this remark de Laet (following Turnebus' translation and followed himself by Hill) proposed to read ὀβέλισκον ἐκ σμαράγδων τεττάρων. But apart from palaeographical considerations, Pliny's interpretation and de Laet's conjecture may be suspected for the following reasons. Theophrastus is thereby made to speak of *one* obelisk made of *four* 'smaragdi'. But (1) *single* obelisks are unknown: they were always erected in one or more pairs. See G. Maspero, *Egyptian Archaeology*, London, 1887, p. 101. Even if on occasion two obelisks of different materials were associated, and there is nothing to suggest that this was ever the case, there is still the objection that (2) obelisks were always *monoliths*. See Gorringe, op. cit., *passim*. Salmasius' reading ('there stand four obelisks of smaragdus') satisfies both these conditions and gives a satisfactory sense to ἀνακεῖσθαι. The *smaragdus* mentioned here may have been green basalt or possibly green Aswan granite.

εὖρος δὲ τῇ μὲν τέτταρας τῇ δὲ δύο. This cannot mean 'four cubits broad in one direction and two cubits broad in the other' since obelisks are square in section, or nearly so. 'Four cubits' is clearly the breadth of the main shaft at the base and 'two cubits' its breadth at the top, beneath the pinnacle, or pyramidion.

The ratio of height (40 cubits) to breadth at base (4 cubits) is not abnormal. The height of the Paris obelisk is 74 ft. 11·2 in. and its breadth at base just under 8 feet. The proportions of Cleopatra's Needle are similar (Gorringe, op. cit., pp. 82–83 and 101), and in general the height is ten times the maximum breadth. The ratio of the breadth at the base of the shaft (4 cubits) to its breadth at the top (2 cubits) is, however, considerably greater than in the Paris and London obelisks, where the figure is approximately 8:5. In the New York obelisk the width at the top of the shaft is said to be two-thirds that of the base (Gorringe, op. cit., p. 61). No measurements are given by Gorringe for the top of the shaft in any instance except the three mentioned above. Thus it is impossible to decide whether Theophrastus has misquoted his authorities or is describing an obelisk in which the tapering of the shaft was more pronounced than in the three examples mentioned. τέτταρας, sc. πήχεις εἶναι.

§ 25. τῶν δὲ Λακαινῶν καλουμένων ὑπὸ πολλῶν. See the critical apparatus. The stone in question must be a green stone known to many people in Greece. Neither (1) τανῶν nor (2) Βακτριανῶν satisfies these conditions. (1) The Persian *tanos* included by Pliny among *smaragdi* (xxxvii. 74) is not likely to have been known as such to many people in Greece at any time. (2) With Βακτριανῶν the question arises, What were these large Bactrian *smaragdi*? They cannot be identified with the small stones found in the Bactrian Desert (§ 35), which were probably blue turquoise. It was a misunderstanding of this latter passage that appears to have given rise to Pliny's seemingly fictitious Bactrian *smaragdi* (see note ad loc.).

The conjecture Λακαινῶν, here printed with some hesitation, fulfils the conditions mentioned above. The stone would be the green porphyry (*verde antico*) known to occur in Greece only at Croceae, on high ground between Mt. Taygetus and the Eurotas, about 15 miles south of Sparta. This stone has a rich green ground speckled with rectangular greenish-white crystals, and occurs not as continuous pieces of rock, but only as pebbles, which are seldom as much as a foot long and a few inches thick (Pausanias iii. 21. 4, and J. G. Frazer, *Pausanias' Description of Greece*, vol. iii, p. 374). One Greek term for green porphyry was Λάκαινα λίθος (Lucian, *Hippias* 5), but Pliny (xxxvii. 73) implies that the smaller pieces could be called Λάκαιναι σμάραγδοι when he mentions *smaragdi* that are dug on Mt. Taygetus. Although the green porphyry of Croceae was little used in Greece during the classical period, it was probably familiar as a curiosity, seeing that it is one of the most colourful stones of the country. The reading Λακαινῶν is discussed more fully in the *Classical Review*, N.S., viii (1958), 221–2.

τοῦ Ἡρακλέους, i.e. Melkarth. Theophrastus may have supposed the block to have consisted of an unusually large piece of green porphyry, but it may in fact have been green jasper or malachite (How and Wells, *A Commentary on Herodotus*, vol. i, p. 188).

γίνεται δὲ ἐν τοῖς ἐν ἐφικτῷ, κτλ. The subject of γίνεται is the *genuine* 'smaragdus', and not the false variety just mentioned. See § 27, ἡ δὲ σμάραγδος σπανία, which shows that from γίνεται to the end of § 27 Theophrastus is concerned with what he believed to be true *smaragdi*. These were not emeralds, of which he shows no knowledge, but green quartz and malachite crystals.

Χαλκηδόνι. The 'island opposite Chalcedon' was Demonesus (mod. Demonesi), which lies in the Sea of Marmora about 12 miles from Scutari. Its copper-mines were famous in antiquity (see [Arist.] *De Mir. Aus.* 834ᵇ), so that ἐν τοῖς χαλκωρυχείοις should be taken with ἐν τῇ νήσῳ κτλ. as well as with περί τε Κύπρον. The manuscript reading Χαρχηδόνι cannot be right because no island in the neighbourhood of Carthage is known to have produced *smaragdi*; and even if this were the case, a Greek would hardly describe such an island as accessible (ἐν ἐφικτῷ).

ἰδιωτέρως. The reading of most manuscripts and editions, ἰδιωτέρους, cannot be correct because (1) Theophrastus probably agreed with Pliny (xxxvii. 72) that the 'smaragdi' of Chalcedon were small and worthless (see note to § 26), and more particularly because (2) the next sentence, μεταλλεύεται γὰρ ὥσπερ τἆλλα, makes it clear that Theophrastus is here concerned not with the quality of the stones, but with the conditions under which they were mined. Hence the reading of E and Turnebus may be accepted with some confidence. For the form ἰδιωτέρως cf. *H.P.* 1. 13. 4. ἐν ταύτῃ refers to Demonesus.

μεταλλεύεται γὰρ ὥσπερ τἆλλα . . . πολλάς. The general sense of this passage is sufficiently clear. Theophrastus is contrasting the *smaragdi* of Demonesus, which were mined like the other minerals of the island (ὥσπερ τἆλλα) and presumably occurred in the same workings, with those of Cyprus, which were found in isolated veins.

The text, however, is corrupt: see the critical apparatus.

Hill and Schneider keep the punctuation and the text of the manuscripts, except that they alter κατὰ ῥάβδους to καὶ ῥάβδους, with Furlanus. But no sense can be made of this, and Furlanus' own translation, 'et in Cypro in venis . . . eruunt', suggests that he would have liked to read κατὰ ῥάβδους ὀρύττουσιν κτλ.

Wimmer, adopting a suggestion made by Schneider in his note on the passage, omits the stop before κατὰ ῥάβδους and prints καὶ ἡ φύσις κατὰ ῥάβδους ἐποίησεν ἐν Κύπρῳ αὐτὴν καθ' αὐτὴν πολλάς, which he translates: 'ac natura in insula Cypro hunc seorsum per multas venas distributum deposuit.' Caley and Richards render this similarly 'and nature has produced it separately in many veins in Cyprus'. But, apart from the drastic alteration of ποιοῦσιν into ἐποίησεν, we should here expect ἡ φύσις to mean not 'Nature', but 'natural substance', 'natural variety', as it does earlier in this section (καὶ γὰρ τοιαύτη γίνεταί τις φύσις).

In the present edition, the text has been emended as follows: a comma is substituted for the colon of the manuscripts before κατὰ ῥάβδους, ποιοῦσιν is changed to τείνουσα and αὐτὴν καθ' αὑτὴν to αὐτὴ καθ' αὑτήν. The whole passage thus reads: μεταλλεύεται γὰρ ὥσπερ τἆλλα καὶ ἡ φύσις, κατὰ ῥάβδους τείνουσα ἐν Κύπρῳ αὐτὴ καθ' αὑτὴν πολλάς, lit. 'For the substance is mined like the other (minerals), while in Cyprus it extends by itself in many veins.' With τείνουσα compare διατείνειν, which is used in a similar context in § 63 and C.P. 4. 12. 6.

§ 26. εὑρίσκονται δὲ σπάνιαι μέγεθος ἔχουσαι σφραγῖδος ἀλλ' ἐλάττους αἱ πολλαί. The bearing of this remark is at first sight not clear. Does it refer (1) to smaragdi in general, or (2) to the smaragdi of Cyprus, or (3) to the smaragdi of Demonesus?

(1) It can hardly refer to smaragdi in general since Theophrastus three times asserts with emphasis that the smaragdus is rare (§ 8, σπάνιοι πάμπαν . . . καθάπερ ἥ τε σμάραγδος . . ., § 24, ἔστι δὲ σπανία, and § 27, ἡ δὲ σμάραγδος σπανία). The smaragdi mentioned here were obviously found in considerable quantities.

(2) Nor is the passage likely to refer to Cyprus, for even though this is the place last mentioned, the reference appears to be merely incidental.

(3) On the other hand, the statement is compatible with Pliny's description of the smaragdi of Chalcedon (xxxvii. 72–73). It is true that he believed the stones to come not from Demonesus, but from a 'mons Smaragdites' in the neighbourhood of Chalcedon itself. Nevertheless, he writes of the stones themselves: 'Calchedonii (sic)—nescio an in totum—exoleverunt postquam metalla aeris ibi defecerunt, et semper tamen uilissimi fuere minimique, iidem fragiles et coloris incerti, etc.'

This interpretation best suits the context as a whole. It adds point to καὶ ἰδιωτέρως εὑρίσκουσιν ἐν ταύτῃ (§ 25) and what follows. Owing to the peculiar conditions under which the smaragdi were found in Demonesus, they were comparatively plentiful, but their quality was poor.

τοῦ χρυσίου here means τοῦ χρυσοῦ: see note on § 59, χρυσίον.

κολλᾷ γάρ. Since they were used, like chrysocolla (here green copper carbonate, malachite), for soldering gold, the smaragdi just mentioned were presumably malachite crystals.

ὥσπερ ἐν τοῖς περὶ ⟨τούτους⟩ τοὺς τόπους. This is the simplest means of restoring the text. ⟨τούτους⟩ τοὺς τόπους will refer to Demonesus and Cyprus (see § 25). Chrysocolla was found in both places (see [Arist.] *De Mir. Aus.* 834ᵇ, chap. 58, for Demonesus, and Pliny xxxiii. 89 for Cyprus).

§ 27. καθάπερ εἴρηται. See §§ 8 and 24.

λίθον ἧς . . . ἴασπις. This specimen may have been partly plasma (*smaragdus*) and partly common chalcedony (*iaspis*). In Pliny (xxxvii. 115–18) *iaspis* seems to be a general term for the less striking varieties of chalcedony, although it is also used of plasma and green jasper.

ὡς οὔπω μεταβεβληκυίας ἀπὸ τοῦ ὕδατος. For a possible explanation of this statement, see pp. 36–38.

CHAPTER V

§ 28. αὕτη τε δὴ περιττὴ τῇ δυνάμει . . . ἕλκει γὰρ ὥσπερ τὸ ἤλεκτρον. This passage is slightly involved, but the sense is clear. αὕτη τε δὴ περιττὴ τῇ δυνάμει refers to the *smaragdus* and its power of imparting a greenish hue to water and of benefiting the eyesight (see § 23). The *lyngurium* (καὶ τὸ λυγγούριον) also has a δύναμις, the power of attraction (ἕλκει γάρ). This last statement is preceded by a parenthesis (καὶ γὰρ ἐκ τούτου . . . στερεωτάτη καθάπερ λίθος) intended to justify the inclusion of the lyngurium among gemstones in spite of the fact that in the opinion of Theophrastus it is not a 'fossile', but an animal secretion. It is so included because (*a*) seals are carved from it, and (*b*) it is as hard as any stone. A similar parenthesis occurs in § 29 in order to justify the inclusion of amber among stones (see the Commentary ad loc.).

οἱ δέ φασιν. See note on § 9, οἱ δὲ . . . λέγουσι.

φύλλα is a conjecture tentatively suggested by Wimmer for ξύλον, on the strength of Pliny's paraphrase (xxxvii. 53, 'nec *folia* tantum aut stramenta ad se rapere, sed aeris etiam ac ferri lamnas, quod Diocli cuidam Theophrastus quoque credit'). ξύλον cannot be right because it must mean a log, billet, plank, something far too bulky to be attracted.

ὥσπερ καὶ Διοκλῆς ἔλεγεν. Pliny (xxxvii. 53) seems doubtful as to the identity of this Diocles, but there can be little doubt that Theophrastus is referring to Diocles of Carystus, the famous physician of the fourth century B.C., whom Pliny praises elsewhere (xxvi. 10) as second only to Hippocrates. Pliny's hesitation was due to his suspicion of the facts recorded here. On the other hand it may be noted that Theophrastus refers to him simply as 'Diocles', which suggests that he had a well-known person in mind. Moreover, it is known that Diocles made a close study of the kidneys and the urinary tract (Galen, *On the Natural Faculties*, I. xiii), and his remarks on the lyngurium no doubt occurred in his discussions on the subject. For the bearing of the reference to Diocles on the dating of the *De Lapidibus*, see pp. 8–9.

ψυχρά is an apt description of yellow and brown tourmaline, which are probably to be identified with the *lyngurium* of Theophrastus. Hill, however, follows Furlanus in reading πυρρά for ψυχρά, an emendation which must have been prompted by Pliny's description (xxxvii. 53) : 'esse autem, qualem in sucinis, *colorem igneum*, scalpique, nec folia tantum aut stramenta ad se rapere, sed aeris etiam ac ferri lamnas, quod Diocli cuidam Theophrastus quoque credit.' In this passage, Theophrastus is made responsible only for the final statement, *nec folia tantum, etc.*, and it seems probable that the detail concerning the colour of the *lyngurium* is derived not from Theophrastus, but from Juba. See M. Wellmann, 'Die Stein- und Gemmenbücher der Antike', pp. 98–99, where the sources of Pliny's statements about *lyngurium* are analysed.

ἢ ξηρότερον τὸ δ᾽ ὑγρότερον. With this phrase understand σῶμα from τοῦ σώματος above. The wild lynxes are 'drier' than the tame ones, the males are 'drier' than the females. For the view that females are 'more moist' than males, see, for example [Arist.] *Problemata* xxxii. 7, 961ᵃ, and Galen, xii, p. 326, Kühn.

κατακρύπτεται. See frag. 175, Wimmer, where Theophrastus denies that this is done from spite.

§ 29. καὶ γὰρ ὀρυκτὸν τὸ περὶ ⟨τὴν⟩ Λιγυστικήν. See the critical apparatus. Wimmer's reading τὸ γὰρ ὀρυκτὸν ὃ περὶ Λιγυστικήν follows closely that of the manuscripts. But it would hardly be relevant to mention at this point that 'fossile amber is that which is found in Liguria'. It would, on the other hand, be relevant to remark that 'the amber found in Liguria is dug', since this would justify the statement that amber is a stone (καὶ τὸ ἤλεκτρον λίθος), and not a secretion of the poplar, as was commonly supposed (see Pliny xxxvii. 31). For καὶ γάρ introducing a parenthesis, cf. § 28, καὶ γὰρ ἐκ τούτου κτλ., and § 38, καὶ γὰρ τοῦθ᾽ ὥσπερ λίθος, where incidentally the points made are similar to that which is intended here. There is no need to follow Schneider in emending ἐπεὶ δὲ καὶ to ἔπειτα καὶ, even though the statement is somewhat elliptical. The literal translation of the sentence is : 'But since amber too is a stone (for that of Liguria is dug), of this too the power of attraction will be an attribute.' This need not mean, as Schneider thought, that amber possesses the power of attraction *because it is a stone*. What Theophrastus wishes to imply is that because amber, like the *lyngurium*, can be regarded as a stone, it too (καὶ τούτῳ) may be included among stones possessing a power of attraction. If it is to be regarded, according to the usual tradition, as a product of the poplar (Arist. *Mete.* 388ᵇ19 ff. and Hdt. iii. 115), then it is not a stone and should not be cited in a treatise on stones. For ἀκολουθεῖν meaning 'to be attribute of', see the note on ἀκολουθεῖ, § 2. The statement should be compared with the similar statement made concerning the *lyngurium* (καὶ γὰρ ἐκ τούτου κτλ., § 28). Even if *lyngurium* is an animal secretion, it may be regarded as a stone because it is very hard and seals are carved from it. If amber is a vegetable product, it cannot be counted as a stone on these grounds because it is not hard and seals are not usually carved from it. A different criterion is therefore found in the fact that some amber at least, the Ligurian, 'is dug from the earth', and is presumably a non-organic substance.

καὶ αὕτη μὲν δὴ . . . ἔχειν. The assurance with which Theophrastus includes the lodestone among stones possessing a power of attraction should be noted. No such confident assertion is made in the case of *lyngurium* and amber because their status as stones is at least debatable.

§ 30. ἡ ὑαλοειδής: perhaps peridot.

τὸ ἀνθράκιον. See § 33 and the note.

ἡ ὄμφαξ: according to Caley and Richards (op. cit., p. 120) prehnite, but perhaps chrysoprase.

ἡ κρύσταλλος: rock-crystal.

τὸ ἀμέθυσον: amethyst.

τὸ σάρδιον. The 'male' is sard, the 'female' carnelian.

ὡς προείρηται πρότερον. Theophrastus has nowhere stated explicitly that there are stones which differ from each other and nevertheless share the same name. But this is the case in §§ 18–19, where two gemstones are cited as having the name ἄνθραξ in common with coal (ἄνθρακες, § 16), and again in § 28, where the stones of the male and female, wild and tame lynx are distinguished, although all are known as λυγγούρια. Theophrastus has also implied that there are true and false *smaragdi* (§ 25).

§ 31. κύανος. See §§ 37, 39; here azurite crystals.

τὸ ὀνύχιον: onyx and perhaps banded agate.

ὁ ἀχάτης: agate, and perhaps especially agate with irregular markings (see Pliny xxxvii. 139). The river Achates has been identified with the Carabi, or Canitello. Numerous agates have been reported from the neighbourhood of Giuliana, which is not far from the head-waters of the river.

§ 32. ἐν Λαμψάκῳ . . . θαυμαστὴ λίθος. There are goldfields 15 miles east of Lampsacus. The stone cannot be identified, but may have been chalcedony or opal. Wimmer prints the rest of the section thus: ἐξ ἧς ἀνενεχθείσης πρὸς στιρὰν (Ἄστυρα Schn.) σφραγίδιον γλυφθὲν ἀνεπέμφθη (Ἀλεξάνδρῳ Plin.) βασιλεῖ διὰ τὸ περιττόν. There are two textual problems to be discussed in this passage: (1) Should Ἀλεξάνδρῳ be inserted on the strength of Pliny's transcription? (2) How is στιρὰν (στιρρὰν) to be emended?

1. Pliny's statement (xxxvii. 193) reads: 'Gemmae nascuntur et repente nouae ac sine nominibus, sicut olim in metallis aurariis Lampsaci unam inuentam, quae propter pulchritudinem Alexandro regi missa sit, auctor est Theophrastus.' Turnebus accepted this statement as evidence that Ἀλεξάνδρῳ should be inserted in the present passage. Schneider and Wimmer more cautiously print the name in brackets. Caley and Richards omit it. It is more than doubtful whether the original text did in fact contain any reference to Alexander. Greek writers do not normally add titles of rank to proper names if the situation is clear without them. Had Theophrastus meant to refer to Alexander, he would presumably have written Ἀλεξάνδρῳ and no more, just as he does in H.P. 4. 4. 1, 4. 4. 5, and 4. 7. 3. The addition of Alexander's name is probably due to Pliny himself. Pliny is apt to add such details to his account so as to make it more circumstantial. For instance, in speaking of the timber of Tylos, an island in the Red Sea, he writes (xvi. 221): 'Alexandri Magni comites prodiderunt . . . .' Turning to Theophrastus, H.P. 5. 4. 7, on which this passage is based, we find simply φασι. Here the addition is justified. But this is not always the case. When Pliny discusses the balsam of Syria, he writes (xii. 117): 'Alexandro res ibi gerente toto die aestiuo unam concham impleri iustum erat.' This passage is derived from H.P. 9. 6. 2, where there is nothing to suggest that the observations were made during Alexander's Syrian campaign. It is therefore not unlikely that Pliny, well aware that Alexander's campaigns had supplied Theophrastus with valuable material, hastily concluded that Alexander was the unnamed recipient of the stone from Lampsacus. Walter Leaf (Strabo on the Troad, p. 96) using Pliny's passage, but ignoring Theophrastus, argues that the stone was a peace-offering to Alexander. In actual fact, it must have been sent to a Persian king (βασιλεῖ), but to which of them, it is useless to inquire, although it may be mentioned that Darius I was on friendly terms with the rulers of Lampsacus (Thuc. vi. 59). It is possible that the source of Theophrastus' story was Anaximenes, an historian who was a native of Lampsacus and a contemporary of Theophrastus (see Pausanias vi. 18. 2–4).

2. While Ἀλεξάνδρῳ may be omitted with confidence, no satisfactory

explanation or emendation of στιρὰν has ever been offered. The phrasing of the sentence throws only a little light on the problem. ἀνενεχθείσης, 'carried up', suggests that the stone was taken up-country into the interior of Asia Minor or Asia, there to be carved into a seal. From there it was sent still further up-country (ἀνεπέμφθη) to the king's court. Thus the place represented in the text by στιρὰν should be looked for at some point on the land-route between Lampsacus and Persia. Unfortunately, none of the readings hitherto suggested satisfies this condition. Stira (if the text is kept unaltered) was a small town in Euboea. Tyra, proposed by de Laet, was a settlement on the Thracian shore of the Euxine. Tira, which occurs in Turnebus' text, appears never to have existed at all. Astyra, suggested by Schneider, lay a short distance inland from Abydos. It was famous for its gold-mines (Strabo xiii. 1. 23) and may perhaps for this reason have been frequented by lapidaries. (It seems likely that lapidaries, who often combined the functions of gem-cutters and metalworkers, worked in the vicinity of the gold- and lead-mines of Britain; see C. E. N. Bromehead, 'Practical Geology in Ancient Britain' (pt. ii), *Proc. Geol. Assoc.* lix (1948), 72–73.) The probable site of Astyra lies some 25 miles south-south-west of Lampsacus. It did not stand on the direct route from Lampsacus to the interior of the Persian empire. Nevertheless, it is the most satisfactory reading available.

For στιρὰν, Rossbach in Pauly–Wissowa, s.v. Gemmen, col. 1055, proposes ἡμέραν. This reading has little or nothing in its favour since ἀναφέρειν πρὸς ἡμέραν is not, as Rossbach supposes, the Greek phrase for 'to bring to light'. We should expect something like πρὸς φῶς ἄγειν (Plato, *Prot.* 320d) or ἐξάγειν εἰς τὸ φῶς (Plato, *Parm.* 128e).

CHAPTER VI

§ 33. The Greek stones mentioned in this section cannot be identified with certainty. The *anthrakion* of Orchomenus and the stone of Chios may have been dark marble, and the stones of Troezen and Corinth serpentine or variegated marble.

§ 34. ἔκ τε Καρχηδόνος καὶ ἐκ τῶν περὶ Μασσαλίαν. See § 18.

Συήνην. See the critical apparatus. This reading gives the required sense: 'from Egypt in the neighbourhood of the Cataract and *of* Syene near the city of Elephantine'. Syene (mod. Aswan) was situated at the First Cataract (οἱ Κατάδουποι), both of them being close to Elephantine and lying within the boundaries of Egypt. Συήνης (i.e. 'from Egypt and *from* Syene') would imply that Syene was not in

Egypt. Theophrastus' description of Syene as being close to Elephantine is true of his time. Up to the Ptolemaic period Elephantine was the more important place (see Hdt. ii. 28, and How and Wells, vol. i, p. 172).

Ψεφώ is presumably identical with 'Psebo' or 'Pseboa', the name of a large lake lying south of Meroe (Strabo xvii. 2. 3). This is Lake Tana in north Abyssinia. See M. Cary and E. H. Warmington, *The Ancient Explorers*, London, 1929, p. 69. The name appears to have several variants (W. L. Lorimer, Pseudo-Aristotle, *De Mundo*, p. 37). It is possible that the stones were Indian, handled, as in later times, by Abyssinian middlemen.

§ 35. οἷς δὲ, κτλ. Pliny (xxxvii. 65) has mistranslated this passage, taking εἰς τὰ λιθοκόλλητα to mean 'in commissuris saxorum', 'in the crevices (joints) of rocks'. Moreover, either he or his authority supposed that Theophrastus must here be referring to *smaragdi*, a gratuitous assumption because the stone last mentioned by Theophrastus is not the *smaragdus*, but the *iaspis*. We presumably have here a reference to certain stones which Theophrastus was unable to name. These were probably blue turquoise, which was much used in Persian inlay work. The famous turquoise mines of Madan in north-east Persia lie 32 miles north of Nishapur and the edge of the great Persian salt desert. The country is called 'Bactriana', perhaps because of some confusion with the Bactrian lapis lazuli from the mines of Badakshan.

τὰ λιθοκόλλητα. Cf. Theophr. *Char.* 23, δεινὸς λέγειν ὡς μετ' Ἀλεξάνδρου ἐστρατεύσατο καὶ ὡς αὐτῷ εἶχε καὶ ὅσα λιθοκόλλητα ποτήρια ἐκόμισε, from which it is clear that Alexander's conquests made this inlaid metalwork familiar to the Greek world. There it attained a considerable vogue (M. Rostovtzeff, *The Social and Economic History of the Hellenistic World*, Oxford, 1941, vol. i, p. 165). Caley and Richards translate τὰ λιθοκόλλητα as 'mosaics', a rendering not even supported by Strabo xvi. 4. 19, which has been cited in this connexion. Mosaics are usually λιθόστρωτα.

τοὺς ἐτησίας. Here the north winds blowing over the Persian desert.

§ 36. τῶν σπουδαζομένων δὲ . . . ταῖς πίνναις. This passage is quoted in full by Athenaeus (iii. 93a–b) and partially by Clement of Alexandria (*Paedag.* ii. 13). For σπουδαζομένων Athenaeus has θαυμαζομένων, a variant which may be ignored in view of his carelessness in quoting.

διαφανὴς μὲν τῇ φύσει. Theophrastus makes a surprising mistake in describing the pearl as transparent. De Laet, following Salmasius, and Hill read οὐ διαφανὴς. On the other hand, both Athenaeus and Clement of Alexandria found διαφανὴς in their texts and apparently accepted it without suspicion. Moreover, their texts differed in one important respect from the extant manuscripts (see note below on πλὴν ἐλάττονι ... εὐμεγέθης), and may therefore be regarded as providing independent support for διαφανής, which is retained in the present text. It is probable that Theophrastus had never seen specimens of the Indian and Arabian pearls. This is the earliest extant reference to the pearl, which was clearly a novelty to Theophrastus since he speaks of it as ὁ μαργαρίτης καλούμενος. If he had to rely upon information and hearsay, one of his informants may have used the term διαυγής, which occurs in the account of Isidorus of Charax (Athenaeus iii. 94a). In this context διαυγής appears to mean 'translucent 'rather than 'transparent', but Theophrastus may have misunderstood the meaning.

παραπλησίῳ. Hill is not justified in emending this to παραπλησίως and translating 'it is produced in a kind of oyster and in like manner in the pinna marina', because παραπλησίως ταῖς πίνναις could not mean this: something like παραπλησίως καὶ ἐν ταῖς πίνναις would be needed. In any case the change is unnecessary because, although Hill is right in stating that the pearl-oyster and the pinna are not similar in shape, they are at least *comparable* in one important respect, namely in possessing a byssus, or silky thread, with which both of them anchor themselves to a convenient rock.

πλὴν ἐλάττονι . . . εὐμεγέθης. Both Athenaeus and Clement of Alexandria continue with this statement after ταῖς πίνναις. It is omitted in all the manuscripts of the *De Lapidibus*. The authenticity of this addition can be neither proved nor disproved, but there is considerable justification for regarding it as genuine. In the first place εὐμεγέθης, which is not common in classical Greek, is used several times by Theophrastus. See *De Lap.*, § 25, *H.P.* 3. 11. 1, 3. 12. 9, 3. 17. 2, 4. 7. 5, and frag. 171, 2, Wimmer. The phrase μέγεθος δὲ ἡλίκον is also characteristic of Theophrastus; cf. *H.P.* 3. 13. 3, 4. 2. 1, and 4. 2. 3. For ἡλίκον in Athenaeus' version, both Schneider and Wimmer read ἡλίκος with Clement. Athenaeus, however, seems to have been correct: ἡλίκον is less grammatical, but more idiomatic than ἡλίκος, as can be seen from *H.P.* 3. 13. 3, where Theophrastus (referring to καρπός) writes τὸ δὲ μέγεθος ἡλίκον κύαμος. For the bearing of this passage upon the state of the extant text, see pp. 13–14.

ἐν τῇ 'Ερυθρᾷ. This term may include the Red Sea, the Persian Gulf, and the Indian Ocean. Here it must refer to the Persian Gulf, the islands being Bahrain and others in the neighbourhood.

§ 37. 'Fossil ivory': probably fossil bones with black and brown mottling, such as have been found at Pikermi in Attica.

Sapphirus: lapis lazuli; 'male' *cyanus*: dark azurite crystals.

πρασῖτις: plasma.

αἱματῖτις: possibly red jasper, but in view of its 'solidity' perhaps haematite.

ξανθή: possibly yellow jasper, but perhaps brown haematite (limonite).

ἔκλευκος. Liddell and Scott⁹ translate 'quite white'. Here it must mean 'whitish', as elsewhere in Theophrastus (*H.P.* 3. 18. 2, &c.).

§ 38. ὁ Ἰνδικὸς κάλαμος ἀπολελιθωμένος: probably the organ-pipe coral.

ταῦτα μὲν οὖν ἄλλης σκέψεως. Theophrastus wrote a work, now lost, 'On Petrifactions' (περὶ τῶν λιθουμένων, Diog. Laert. v. 42). The correct title was probably περὶ τῶν ἀπολιθουμένων. See W. Jaeger, *Diokles von Karystos*, p. 115. Jaeger points out that petrifaction was of considerable interest to the Peripatetics, as is shown by *Probl.* xxiv. 11. 837ᵃ11 ff. and *De Mir. Aus.* 834ᵃ27–28 and 838ᵃ14.

CHAPTER VII

§ 39. ἔνιαι . . . μόνον ἄργυρον: probably veins of galena, the 'gold' being iron pyrites.

καὶ κύανος . . . χρυσοκόλλαν: azurite (blue copper carbonate) with malachite (green copper carbonate).

βάρος δ' ἔχουσα. If the manuscript reading βάρος δ' ἔχουσι is kept, the statement must refer both to the *cyanus* and to the charcoal-like stone. But in this case we should expect βάρος δὲ καὶ αὗται ἔχουσι, i.e. these stones too are heavy, like the heavy (βαρύτεραι . . . τῇ ῥοπῇ) stones just mentioned. βάρος δ' ἔχουσα, on the other hand, contrasts naturally with ὁμοία τὴν χρόαν τοῖς ἄνθραξι, i.e. there is another stone, similar in colour to charcoal, but heavy. Schneider was uncertain whether τοῖς ἄνθραξι referred to coal or to the precious stone of that name. Theophrastus, however, refers to the precious stone in the singular (§§ 18–19), while the plural denotes coal or charcoal (see § 16, and *De Igne*, 23, 58, 71, 75). Charcoal, and not coal, must be the meaning here, since to convey the sense 'coal' οἱ ἄνθρακες would need to be qualified, as in § 16. Caley and Richards here translate τοῖς ἄνθραξι as 'glowing coals', but in this case we should expect such a phrase as § 18, ἄνθρακος καιομένου. This stone is possibly pyrolusite (manganese dioxide).

§ 40. For the transference of τὸ ὅλον . . . ὅμοια τούτοις to § 50, see the Commentary ad loc.

For λάβοι, 'find', see note on λάβοι, § 60.

§ 41. ἔνιαι δὲ λίθοι . . . λίθοις ἑτέροις. This refers primarily to gem-stones, which could be effectively carved only by means of 'other stones'. Gem-engravers in antiquity relied mainly on three tools, a diamond- or white sapphire-point, a bronze drill coated with particles of emery, and a bronze wheel, also coated with emery particles (J. H. Middleton, *Engraved Gems of Classical Times* (Cambridge, 1891), pp. 103–14). According to M. B. Walters, *Engraved Gems and Cameos in the British Museum*, 1926, p. xx, 'the diamond point is not often employed, owing to the rarity of diamonds, at any rate before Hellenistic times'. There is no reason to suppose that Theophrastus is alluding to the diamond, as Walters seems to think. For Theophrastus, emery is *par excellence* the stone which the gem-engraver uses (§ 44).

ὥσπερ εἴπομεν. See §§ 4 and 5.

καὶ τῶν μειζόνων λίθων. J. H. Middleton, op. cit., p. 106, footnote 1, writes: 'In this passage the word μειζόνων is probably corrupt, since the *size* of gems has nothing to do with their relative *hardness*.' But the examples that follow (the μαγνῆτις and the Siphnian stone) show that Theophrastus has shifted his attention from gemstones to larger stones which are not precious.

καθάπερ ἐλέχθη. See § 5.

ἡ μαγνῆτις αὕτη λίθος. For the demonstrative, ignored by Caley and Richards, cf. § 61, τὰς λίθους τὰς ἐκ τῆς Ἀσίας ταύτας ἀγομένας, and *H.P.* 3. 7. 3, 3. 18. 11, and 4. 7. 1. Wimmer's translation is 'lapis ille magnes'. Similarly τὸ θυλακῶδες τοῦτο, *H.P.* 3. 7. 3, is translated by Sir Arthur Hort in the Loeb edition 'the familiar bag-like thing'. But in a footnote to *H.P.* 3. 18. 11 Hort asks, 'Is the pronoun deictic, referring to an actual specimen shewn in lecture?' This certainly seems to be the case in *H.P.* 4. 7. 1, where the plants mentioned come from 'the outer sea near the pillars of Hercules', and can hardly have been familiar. A pure specimen of *magnetis* (talc) such as is described in the present passage is not likely to have been familiar, let alone the artificial stones from Asia of § 61. Therefore the demonstratives here and in § 61 may be translated literally. We assume that specimens were shown in both instances. Many other specimens must have been shown, but references to them were no doubt usually excised in the course of editing. The description of the *magnetis* points to foliated talc.

§ 42. The Siphnian stone is likely to have been steatite.

§ 43. οἱ μὲν τοιοῦτοι. There is no need to supply οὖν with Schneider, Wimmer, and Caley and Richards since the demonstrative pronoun itself acts as a link. See J. D. Denniston, *The Greek Particles*, p. xliv. For other instances in Theophrastus see *H.P.* 5. 9. 4, εἰς μὲν τὴν ἀνθρακίαν τὰ τοιαῦτα ζήτουσι, 6. 3. 6 (end), and 6. 6. 2 (end).

σιδηρίοις is read here and in the next sentence instead of σιδήροις, which appears in the manuscripts and previous editions. Cf. § 41, σιδηρίοις, and § 5, σιδήριον. Liddell and Scott[9] cite only one instance of σίδηρος in the plural, namely Theocritus xxi. 49, where it means 'fish-hooks', not 'iron tools'.

καθάπερ εἴπομεν. See § 41.

οἱ δὲ σιδηρίοις . . . σκληρότερος ὤν. The manuscripts are hopelessly corrupt.

1. οἱ δὲ σιδηρίοις μὲν ἀμ⟨βλυτέροις⟩ δέ. This, the conjecture of Turnebus which is adopted by Schneider, Wimmer, and Caley and Richards, offers a reasonable solution. Cf. Pliny xxxvii. 200, 'iam tanta differentia est, ut aliae ferro scalpi non possint, aliae non nisi retuso'.

2. καὶ εἰσὶν is followed in A by a lacuna of about nine letters. No solution has been offered. καὶ εἰσὶν ⟨ἄλλαι διαφοραί⟩?

3. παραπλησίως δὲ κάτω. Wimmer writes : 'in voce κάτω latere ἄτοπον puto', a highly plausible suggestion seeing that § 44 begins with ἄτοπον δὲ κἀκεῖνο. But it is more likely that κάτω conceals καὶ ἄτοπον.

4. τα* μὴ τέμνεσθαι σιδήρῳ. In A there is a lacuna of seven letters between τα and μή. Next we may notice τέμνεσθαι. This is the technical term for 'to be quarried' : cf. μέγας τέμνεται, §§ 6 and 65. Theophrastus has mentioned that some stones are not *carved* by iron. Now presumably he alludes to 'the almost equally strange fact (παραπλησίως δὲ καὶ ἄτοπον) that some stones are not *quarried* by iron'. If this is so, we may read τὸ for τα and then supply ἐνίους (sc. λίθους). Cf. § 43, ἔνιοι.

5. καίτοι καὶ στερεὸν ἔτε is followed in A by a lacuna of about six letters. In the present text τὰ is read for καὶ, followed by στερεώτερα ⟨ὅλως⟩ ἰσχυρότερον τέμνει καὶ ⟨ὁ⟩ σίδηρος λίθου (Turnebus, for λίθους) σκληρότερος ὤν, i.e. 'and yet in general the more recalcitrant substances are cut more strongly by iron, which is harder than stone'. With καίτοι τὰ στερεώτερα ⟨ὅλως⟩ cf. *De Igne* 32, καίτοι θερμότατόν γε πῦρ ὅλως. For ἰσχυρός used of the strength of instruments see *C.P.* 3. 20. 8, Θετταλοὶ δ' ἰσχυρότερον . . . ὄργανον ἔχουσιν.

With the structure of the passage as thus restored we may compare that of *De Sudore* 36, ἄτοπον δ' ὅτι οἱ ἀγωνιῶντες τοὺς πόδας ἱδρῶσι, τὸ δὲ πρόσωπον οὔ. καίτοι μᾶλλον εὔλογον τὸ μάλισθ' ἱδρωτικὸν καὶ μὴ τὸ ἥκιστα, where similarly ἄτοπον introduces a paradox, and καίτοι brings in as a contrast what would be expected as normal.

§ 44. ἄτοπον δὲ κἀκεῖνο . . . ἐξ ἧς δ' αἱ σφραγῖδες οὔ. Theophrastus here presents us with a double paradox:

1. A whetstone, in grinding iron, wears it down (κατεσθίει), but iron

in its turn can split and shape (δύναται διαιρεῖν καὶ ῥυθμίζειν) a whet-stone.

Thus each substance has the capacity to act on the other and also to react to it, or, as Theophrastus would say, δυνάμεις τοῦ τε ποιεῖν καὶ τοῦ πάσχειν (see § 4).

2. Iron can split and shape a whetstone, but has no such effect on a gemstone (ἐξ ἧς δ᾽ αἱ σφραγῖδες οὔ: with ἐξ ἧς supply λίθου).

Why this should be considered paradoxical is not immediately clear. We may suppose that Theophrastus reasoned as follows:

(a) Iron is worn down by a whetstone; therefore a whetstone must be extremely hard, at least as hard as any other stone.

(b) But iron can split and shape a whetstone.

(c) We should therefore expect iron to be able to split and shape all other stones.

(d) And yet it has no such effect on a gemstone.

καὶ πάλιν ὁ λίθος . . . ἐξ οὗπερ αἱ ἀκόναι. This sentence introduces another paradox: Furthermore (πάλιν) the whetstone (which is split by iron) is identical with, or similar to, the stone used for carving gemstones. It is therefore all the more surprising that iron has no effect on gemstones. The whetstone referred to here was probably emery.

ἄγεται δὲ ἡ ⟨βελτίστη⟩ ἐξ Ἀρμενίας. Schneider and Wimmer supply ἀρίστη since otherwise the statement is meaningless. But βελτίστη is preferable: see the apparatus. This addition is suggested by Pliny xxxvi. 54: 'Naxium diu placuit ante alia . . . uicere postea ex Armenia inuectae.' Emery has been found in Russian Armenia some 30 miles south of Elisavetpol (the name has probably been altered since 1912, the date of this information). The local source is Naxos.

§ 45. τῆς βασανιζούσης τὸν χρυσόν. The touchstone has already been alluded to in § 4 as ἡ Λυδή (λίθος).

The colour of pure gold is not altered by fire. See Pliny xxxiii. 59, 'aurique experimentum ignis est, ut simili colore rubeat ignescatque et ipsum; obrussam uocant.' Impure gold changes colour according to the metal alloyed with it. Gold containing silver turns pale; gold alloyed with lead is blackened; while gold alloyed with copper or zinc becomes reddish. See E. O. von Lippmann, Entstehung und Ausbreitung der Alchemie, vol. i, p. 7.

ἀλλοιοῦν. The present editor follows Turnebus and recent editors in adopting the reading of E, ἀλλοιοῦν. Schwarze (De Lapide Lydio, Görlitz, 1805–6) defends ἀξιοῦν, for which he offers the rendering 'verum auri indicans pretium'. The word, however, can hardly bear this meaning by itself; it occasionally means 'to value', but seems to require a genitive of price. In any case, the fire can hardly be said to value the gold except in a figurative sense. Although ἀλλοιοῦν does little more than repeat μεταβάλλειν, a similar tautology occurs in *C.P.* 5. 9. 3, ἐν δὲ τῇ ἐκστάσει μεταβολὴ καὶ ἀλλοίωσις, and in *C.P.* 6. 7. 1, μεταβολαί γε καὶ ἀλλοιώσεις καὶ ἐν ἐκείνοις εἰσὶ τῶν χυλῶν.

τῇ παρατρίψει, 'rubbing alongside'; cf. Hdt. vii. 10, ἐπεὰν δὲ παρατρίψωμεν ἄλλῳ χρυσῷ, διαγινώσκομεν τὸν ἀμείνω. The gold to be tested was rubbed on a touchstone already marked by a streak made by gold known to be pure. The new streak could thus be compared with the original one, and the relative impurity of the specimen under test detected by the different appearance of the streak left by it on the stone.

§ 46. τὸν ἐκ τῆς καθάρσεως, sc. χρυσόν: cf. Hdt. loc. cit., τὸν χρυσὸν τὸν ἀκήρατον, and Theognis 449, χρυσὸς ἄπεφθος.

χρυσὸν καὶ ἄργυρον. Cf. § 4, τὸν χρυσὸν καὶ τὸν ἄργυρον, and the Commentary.

πόσον εἰς τὸν στατῆρα μέμικται. According to W. Ridgeway (*Numismatic Chronicle*, 3rd series, xv (1895), 105) the Attic stater weighed 135 grains troy (8·747 grammes). Ridgeway also maintains (*Metallic Currency*, pp. 307–8) that the stater, and not the talent, which weighed 3,000 times as much, was the standard unit of the Greek system of weights. This view receives some support from the present passage. On the other hand a unit smaller than the talent was obviously desirable in dealing with precious metals, and it would be dangerous to conclude that the stater was the normal commercial unit.

σημεῖα are the streaks made by specimens in which the proportion of alloy to precious metal varied, but was in each case known beforehand. These streaks formed a graded scale with which the streak made by the specimen under test could be compared. This scale started 'with the smallest quantity' (ἀπὸ τοῦ ἐλαχίστου), that is, with the mixture containing the smallest quantity of the alloy.

ἐλάχιστον δὲ γίνεται . . . ἢ ἡμιωβόλιον. See the critical apparatus. M. N. Tod (*Numismatic Chronicle*, 5th series, v (1945), 4, n. 1) states that ἡμιώβολος (read here by Schneider, Wimmer, and Caley and Richards) should be emended to ἡμιώβολον or ἡμιωβόλιον. Of these the second is closer to the manuscript readings. Ridgeway (*Numismatic Chronicle*, 3rd series, xv (1895) 105–7) shows that the κριθή (barleycorn) weighed 0·0606 gramme, being almost identical with the grain troy (English barleycorn), which weighs 0·064 gramme. There were 12 κριθαί and 8 κόλλυβοι to an obol. We thus obtain the following table:

1 krithe			= 0·0606 gramme
1½ krithae	= 1 kollybos		= 0·0909 ,,
3 ,,	= 1 tetartemorion (quarter-obol)		= 0·182 ,,
6 ,,	= hemiobolion (half-obol)		= 0·364 ,,
12 ,,	= 1 obol		= 0·728 ,,
72 ,,	= 1 drachm	(?)	= 4·368 ,,
144 ,,	= 1 stater		= 8·747 ,,
			(or 8·736?)

According to the usual text the scale of streaks will start with a streak representing a mixture which contains one krithe of alloy in each stater. In this case we must suppose that the technique of testing had attained an incredible degree of accuracy. A krithe is 1/144th of a stater, so that the superior type of touchstone which Theophrastus is discussing would actually be capable of detecting accurately an alloy which formed only 1/144th of the whole. Ridgeway (*Numismatic Chronicle*, loc. cit., p. 108) is prepared to accept this startling conclusion. But this is not the worst. The next streak in the scale must, according to the common reading, represent a mixture containing a kollybos of alloy in each stater. Now a kollybos is 1/96th of a stater, so that the difference between a krithe and a kollybos must be 1/288th of a stater. And yet this minute difference in the composition of two mixtures of metal would, we must suppose, also be detected accurately by the touchstone! Even if we allow for the exaggerated claims of enthusiastic professionals, it is hardly probable that Theophrastus would have mentioned them without a cautionary comment.

Consequently Schwarze (*De Lapide Lydio*) was amply justified in supposing that that part of the passage at least which refers to the smaller weights (κριθή, εἶτα κόλλυβος, εἶτα . . .) was inserted from a gloss mistakenly intended to explain what was meant by 'the smallest account' (ἐλάχιστον), this being the handiwork of a commentator who knew that the smallest weights in general use were the krithe and the kollybos, but did not understand that they had no relevance here. The manuscript reading κριθῆν . . . κόλυμβον suggests that the writer of the gloss took ἐλάχιστον and τεταρτημόριον to be accusatives.

A quarter-obol is 1/48th of a stater and a half-obol 1/24th. Consequently if Schwarze's suggestion is adopted, the first streak will indicate a mixture containing base metal to the extent of 1/48th or 1/24th of the whole. Or, to use the modern standard, the gold will be of 23½ or 23 carat. Possibly two scales were in use, one indicating differences of 1 carat, and the other, employed by more ambitious members of the profession, indicating differences of half a carat. These orders of magnitude are not only more feasible than the fractions of 1/144th and 1/288th involved in the original reading, but also appear to be confirmed by modern experience. C. G. E. Bunt (*'Chaffers' Handbook to Hall Marks on Gold and Silver Plate*, 7th edition, p. 7) writes of the test by touchstone: 'It has been said that the difference of half a carat can be distinguished in this way.'

§ 47. **εὑρίσκονται δὲ τοιαῦται πᾶσαι ἐν τῷ ποταμῷ Τμώλῳ.** Nothing further is known of a *river* Tmolus. Theophrastus must have meant the Pactolus or some other river in Lydia rising on Mt. Tmolus. For a similar mistake, see Juvenal, *Sat.* vi. 409–12, where Mt. Niphates is described as a river. Touchstones are usually black siliceous slate.

μέγεθος δὲ ὅσον διπλασία τῆς μεγίστης ψήφου. Theophrastus has just stated that the touchstone is like a ψῆφος, and that it is flat and not round. Now he adds that its size is roughly twice that of the largest ψῆφος. It is difficult to make any inferences without knowing what Theophrastus meant by the term, and of this he gives no hint. Pliny is more helpful, for he states (xxxiii. 126) that the touchstone is of moderate size 'quaternas uncias longitudinis binasque latitudinis non excedentes', i.e. not exceeding 4 inches in length and 2 inches in breadth. On the strength of Pliny's statement we may suppose that Theophrastus had in mind a ψῆφος of 2 inches in diameter, the touchstone being elliptical, with a minor axis of 2 inches and a major axis of twice this length, so that it might be assumed to be roughly double the ψῆφος in size. A ψῆφος 2 inches in diameter would of course be an extremely large counter, if we are to assume that a counter is what is here meant by the word. But Theophrastus expressly states that the touchstone is twice the size of the *largest* ψῆφος. As an alternative it might be argued that a voting-disk, such as was used in the law-courts of Athens, is here referred to. But these disks, if a fair ballot was to be ensured, must have been as uniform in size as careful craftsmanship could have made them. No voting-disk could have been described as 'largest'.

Counters such as were used in calculations were no doubt so common in antiquity that no detailed description was needed. Hence the vagueness of Theophrastus' remarks.

ὡς ἰδίοντος τοῦ ἔδους. This reading had already been adopted in the present text when it was discovered in the margin of the British Museum's copy of Turnebus' text of 1577. The writer of the note is not known. σημεῖον ('a portent') occurs in *H.P.* 4. 16. 3, and ἰδίειν in *H.P.* 5. 9. 8. In the latter passage Theophrastus describes a similar manifestation produced by wooden images.

CHAPTER VIII

§ 48. διαφοραὶ καὶ δυνάμεις. In § 4 δυνάμεις are regarded as a sub-division of διαφοραί, for there Theophrastus speaks of αἱ κατὰ τὰς δυνάμεις κτλ., sc. διαφοραί. In the present passage he distinguishes the two concepts, no doubt for the sake of convenience, since more attention has been paid to the δυνάμεις than to the other διαφοραί. This is particularly the case in chaps. II, III, V, and VII. Here, in § 48, διαφοραί must refer to such qualities as colour, smoothness, and solidity, which in § 3 are contrasted with the qualities conferred by the δυνάμεις ('capacities').

τὸ μὲν γὰρ τήκεσθαι καὶ μαλάττεσθαι. Aristotle uses τήκεσθαι both of melting by heat (Mete. 383ᵃ28, 32; 383ᵇ5, 7) and of dissolving in liquids (Mete. 383ᵇ14, twice). Theophrastus here and below (τήκεται) and in §§ 9 and 61 uses the word in the former sense. Although Aristotle uses μαλάττεσθαι of softening iron by heat (Mete. 378ᵇ17; 383ᵃ31), both here and in § 61 the word must refer to the softening or 'puddling' of clay in water before it is fired. Caley and Richards are not correct in stating (op. cit., p. 159) that 'in this context the verb τήκεσθαι really describes a softening caused by the action of water, and μαλάττεσθαι means a softening caused by the action of heat'. The latter remark is inconsistent with their note on μαλάττεται, p. 161, in which they write that 'clay was first "softened" by water'.

In explaining τήκεσθαι Theophrastus could have mentioned that earths dissolve, or rather disintegrate, in water, but this is one of their most obvious qualities (see the Commentary on ὑπὸ πυρός, § 3), and here he is concerned with more uncommon qualities.

τήκεται μὲν γὰρ ⟨ἅμα⟩ τοῖς χυτοῖς καὶ ὀρυκτοῖς, ὥσπερ καὶ ὁ λίθος. Cf. § 9, where slag is described as fusing with silver, copper, and iron. An example of an earth behaving in similar fashion is given in § 49, where we seem to find an allusion to the fusing of cadmia with copper to form brass. ⟨ἅμα⟩ τοῖς χυτοῖς καὶ ὀρυκτοῖς, lit. 'along with things fused (smelted) and dug', a case of hysteron proteron: cf. πυροῦντες καὶ μαλάττοντες, below, and for other examples §§ 58, 59, 61. ὀρυκτοῖς is here used of the metals, whereas in § 1 Theophrastus follows Aristotle in describing them as τὰ μεταλλευόμενα. But Theophrastus does not observe Aristotle's distinction (Mete. 378ᵃ20 ff.) between τὰ μεταλλευτά or τὰ μεταλλευόμενα (metals) and τὰ ὀρυκτά ('fossiles', minerals). In § 61 he uses τῶν μεταλλευτῶν of earths. See p. 4.

λίθους τε ποιοῦσιν. Hill, following Furlanus, reads πλίνθους τε ποιοῦσιν. Possibly Theophrastus was referring to bricks, but ποικίλας shows that they could not have been ordinary bricks (cf. § 61, where they seem to be mentioned again). Moreover λίθους is echoed by πρὸς τὴν ἀπολίθωσιν in § 50.

πυροῦντες καὶ μαλάττοντες. For the *hysteron proteron*, see the examples just quoted.

§ 49. ὥς τινές φασι. Theophrastus is cautious in putting forward what is substantially a correct explanation of the manufacture of glass. It is probable that the facts had only recently become known in Greece. See p. 36, n. 2. Hill seems to have been justified in reading πυρώσει, echoing πυροῦντες. The manuscript reading πυκνώσει ('by thickening') introduces an irrelevancy.

ἰδιωτάτη δ' ἡ τῷ χαλκῷ, κτλ. This seems to refer to the fusing of what was later known as *cadmia* (calamine) with copper to form brass. In Theophrastus' day the process was a mystery and perhaps confined to Pontus. See [Aristotle] *De Mir. Aus.* 835ᵃ, ch. 62, a passage which may be derived from Theophrastus' lost work *De Metallis*.

περὶ δὲ Κιλικίαν, κτλ. This 'vine-earth' was a hard variety of asphalt.

§ 50. εἴη δ' ἂν, κτλ. Earths may be considered according to (1) their aptness to harden to the consistency of stone, (2) their taste, or (3) their colour. The third method is the one adopted. λαμβάνειν may mean 'consider', as in Arist. *Mete.* 341ᵃ25 and 347ᵇ34, but more probably means 'find', as in §§ 40 and 60.

αἵ γε τοὺς τούτων. There is no need to alter τούτων to τῶν τόπων, as Wimmer and others have done, following Turnebus' translation. τούτων refers to the earths. With αἵ γε . . . ποιοῦσαι, supply διαφοραί: with αἱ τοὺς τῶν φυτῶν supply ποιοῦσαι χυμοὺς διαφόρους ἀλλήλων.

§ 50 (40). χρῶνται . . . καὶ γάρ. At this point in the present text the passage τὸ ὅλον . . . ὅμοια τούτοις, forming the greater part of § 40, has been inserted. This passage contains the names of six mineral earths, whereas chapter VII, where it has hitherto appeared, is devoted to stones. In its original position it is clearly out of place. Here it is entirely appropriate. τῶν τοιούτων will refer to the coloured earths hinted at above (ἀλλὰ μᾶλλον . . . χρῶνται). All the earths mentioned here are notable for their colour. The passage will also explain τούτων below (καὶ γὰρ ἡ γένεσις τούτων).

ὧν τὰ μέν . . . τὰ δ' . . . τὰ δὲ . . ., i.e. ochre (yellow ochre) and ruddle (red ochre) are composed of earth, chrysocolla (massive malachite) and *cyanus* (here massive azurite) of a kind of sand, realgar and orpiment of powder. Here Theophrastus is criticizing Aristotle, who had maintained (*Mete.* 378ᵃ21–26) that not only realgar, but also ochre and ruddle, and indeed most 'fossiles' were coloured powder. See p. 47.

§ 50. ὥσπερ ἐξ ἀρχῆς εἴπομεν. There is no explicit statement in the introduction to the effect that these earths are formed either by a 'conflux' or by 'filtering'. The assertions which are made here by Theophrastus are discussed on p. 25.

ἀπὸ τῆς ἀναθυμιάσεως . . . τῆς ξηρᾶς καὶ καπνώδους. For 'the dry smoky exhalation' see pp. 38, 43–44, 46–47.

§ 51. τῶν μέν εἰσι ῥάβδοι, τὴν δ' ὤχραν ἀθρόαν, κτλ. See p. 25. τοὺς γραφεῖς. See the critical apparatus. τοὺς βαφεῖς cannot be right because the earths are being discussed with reference to their use as *painters'* pigments (§ 50). Dyeing is nowhere mentioned. τὰ ἀνδρείκελα were flesh-coloured pigments used in painting (Plato, *Crat.* 424e) and also as cosmetics (Xenophon, *Oec.* x. 5–6).

διὰ τὸ μηδὲν τῇ χρόᾳ διαφέρειν, δοκεῖν δέ. This is an obscure statement. We are perhaps to suppose that ochre does not differ in colour from orpiment when it has been prepared or possibly applied, but that it does differ in its natural state and in its texture. This is substantially true. And yet it is difficult to imagine that ochre could ever equal orpiment in brilliance.

§ 52. χαλεπὸν δὲ . . . τὸ πνίγεσθαι. The air would soon become exhausted in the narrow workings. Theophrastus wrote a monograph 'On Suffocation' (περὶ πνιγμοῦ: see frag. 166, Wimmer).

ἐν δὲ τῷ μικρῷ ⟨μετάλλῳ⟩ μεταλλεύεται καθ' αὑτήν. In the manuscripts this sentence begins § 53 after εἰς Σινώπην, but it has been transposed in the present edition so as to provide an antithesis to ἡ μὲν οὖν κτλ.: 'The best ruddle—for there are many kinds—seems to be that of Ceos. Some of it comes from the mines, for iron mines also contain ruddle, but in the small (mine) it is worked by itself.' Nothing definite is known of a small working such as this, but the following description fits Theophrastus' statement admirably: 'At Spathi east of the town of Ceos are ancient stopes and galleries, the latter about 4 feet high by 3 feet wide, cut with a gad. The exploitation is small and there is no slag, suggesting that the ore was required not for smelting, but as a pigment' (O. Davis, *Roman Mines in Europe*, p. 257). Hill's reading ἐν δὲ τῇ Λήμνῳ, which was first suggested by Furlanus, is palaeographically unconvincing. The present reading, however, is open to the objection that one would expect ἐν δὲ τῷ μικρῷ καλουμένῳ μετάλλῳ.

§ 53. αὐτῆς refers to ruddle as a whole, not to the last kind mentioned. Cf. *H.P.* 7. 4. 5, ὡσαύτως δὲ καὶ τῆς θριδακίνης· ἡ γὰρ λευκὴ γλυκυτέρα καὶ ἀπαλωτέρα· γένη δὲ αὐτῆς ἐστιν ἄλλα τρία.

ταύτην αὐτάρκη καλοῦμεν. For the asyndeton, cf. § 43, οἱ μὲν τοιοῦτοι and the Commentary. ταύτην presumably refers to the medium shade (ἡ μέση) last mentioned, with which the deeper and the paler shades each had to be mixed because in their natural state the former was too dark and the latter too light.

τὸ δ' εὕρημα Κυδίου. This Cydias was probably the painter of that name. He was a contemporary of Euphranor (Pliny xxxv. 130), who flourished about 364 B.C. (Pliny xxxv. 128).

παντοπωλίου. Cf. Plato, *Rep.* 557d.

§ 54. χύτρας καινὰς περιπλάσαντες πηλῷ. See the critical apparatus. The emended text is supported by Pliny xxxv. 35, 'ea et fit ochra exusta in ollis nouis luto circumlitis'. περιπλάσαντες πηλῷ, i.e. 'luting' them, sealing the lids with clay. This use of περιπλάττειν is illustrated by Dioscorides v. 81, Wellmann, περιπλάσαντες τὸ πῶμα καὶ ὀλίγην δόντες ἀναπνοήν. Cf. also Theophr. *De Igne* 43, περιπωματίζοντες καὶ περιπλάττοντες.

μαρτυρεῖ δ' . . . νομίζειν: lit. 'The process of generation itself confirms this. For it is by fire that all these (substances) would appear to be altered, if indeed we are to suppose that their generation here (i.e. their production by artificial means) is similar to, or comparable with, the natural mode of generation.' ἅπαντα ταῦτα, i.e. the mineral earths, ochre, ruddle, &c., at present under discussion. 'Fired' cyanus is mentioned in § 55. The argument may be paraphrased as follows: That ruddle can be produced artificially in the manner described is not strange: the facts are indeed corroborated by the way in which the ruddle is produced. Fire (or, more precisely, the dry, smoky exhalation, the nature of which is fiery) is the efficient cause when ruddle, &c., are generated *naturally*, as was implied in § 50. Why, then, should fire not produce similar substances artificially, seeing that the artificial process must be similar to, or at least comparable with, the natural process? This is a somewhat peculiar argument. A modern scientist would be inclined to use his observation of the artificial and familiar process as a means of drawing conclusions as to the natural and unfamiliar process. Theophrastus' procedure is the reverse. What is known of the natural process is used to corroborate the facts of the artificial process, even though his theory regarding the natural process is only to a limited extent based on direct observation. See § 50, καὶ ἔνιά γε δὴ φαίνεται πεπυρωμένα καὶ οἷον κατακεκαυμένα, and the comments on this remark on pp. 46–47. To Theophrastus himself, this procedure must have appeared reasonable enough. 'Art imitates Nature' (§ 60), but this does not necessarily entitle us to argue as if Nature imitated Art.

ὁμοίαν ἢ παραπλησίαν. Cf. Thuc. i. 140, ὁρῶ δὲ καὶ νῦν ὅμοια καὶ παραπλήσια ξυμβουλευτέα μοι ὄντα.

§ 55. In this passage the natural *cyanus* is massive azurite, while the artificial is Egyptian frit.

οἱ γράφοντες τὰ περὶ τοὺς βασιλεῖς. Cf. § 24, ταῖς ἀναγραφαῖς κτλ. and the Commentary.

χυτόν, 'fused', makes good sense. The artificial *cyanus* was produced by fusing certain ingredients so as to form a vitreous mass, which was then finely ground. τεχνητόν, Furlanus' emendation, is unnecessary.

τοῦ μὲν ἀπύρου τοῦ δὲ πεπυρωμένου. The 'fireless' *cyanus* is the natural kind, the 'fired' the artificial. Theophrastus does not mean to imply that the 'fired' *cyanus* was roasted, as the ochre of § 54 was roasted. See the last note. Roasted *cyanus* would merely turn black and have no commercial value.

τὸν Σκύθην κύανον has the support of Pliny xxxiii. 161, 'Scythicum mox diluitur facile et, cum teritur, in quattuor colores mutatur.' The manuscript reading τὸν μὲν κύανον is corrupt because there is nothing to correspond to μέν. There is a similarly puzzling μέν in § 69. In both passages it appears to be used as a stopgap. See *Classical Review*, N.S., ii (1952), 144–5.

§ 56. ἀπηθοῦσιν. In the manufacture of white lead, water would be poured on the scrapings and strained away; cf. *H.P.* 9. 8. 3. If the lead scrapings were beaten to powder in the open air and treated with water that was 'hard', lead acetate would be converted, though incompletely, into lead carbonate.

§ 57. χαλκὸς ἐρυθρός (red copper) is pure copper, as opposed to bronze. Some verdigris would be produced by copper exposed to wine-lees, but the process would be extremely slow. Caley and Richards (op. cit., p. 191) may therefore be right in interpreting τρύξ as grape-residues 'in a state of acetous fermentation'.

⟨ἐπεὶ⟩ ἐπιφαίνεται γινόμενος ⟨ὁ ἰός⟩. See the critical apparatus. Wimmer's text gives reasonable sense, but has no manuscript support. τιθέμενος might well have been substituted for γινόμενος by a scribe whose eye wandered to τίθεται. The omission of ὁ ἰός might have been a haplographical error. The passage cannot be emended satisfactorily.

§ 58. τὸ περὶ 'Ιβηρίαν. At this time 'Ιβηρία, unqualified, must mean Spain, and not Georgia, as Caley and Richards, op. cit., pp. 195–6, maintain. See Aristotle, *De Generatione Animalium* 748ᵃ26; [Arist.] *De Mir. Aus.* 837ᵃ24, 31, ᵇ6, 844ᵃ4. The cinnabar deposits of Georgia are probably included in the phrase τὸ ἐν Κόλχοις. Caley and Richards (loc. cit.) maintain that the Spanish deposits were probably discovered and certainly exploited later than those near Ephesus; and in support of this view they cite Vitruvius, vii. 8, 1 and vii. 9, 4: 'id autem agris Ephesiorum Cilbianis primum esse memoratur inuentum . . . quae autem in Ephesiorum metallis fuerunt officinae nunc traiectae sunt ideo Romam quod id genus uenae postea est inuentum Hispaniae regionibus, ⟨e⟩ quibus metallis glaebae portantur et per publicanos Romae curantur.' But this garbled statement should not be allowed to interfere with the natural interpretation of Theophrastus. On the contrary, it is reasonable to allow Theophrastus' statement to qualify that of Vitruvius. From this latter statement, we should merely infer that the Roman authorities became interested in exploiting Spanish cinnabar when they had for some time been exploiting the deposits near Ephesus.

μικρὸν ⟨ἐν Κιλβιανοῖς⟩. See the next note but one.

ὁ κόκκος. The kermes-berry, from which a red dye is made, is really an insect, but this fact was not known in antiquity.

[μικρὸν ἐν καλοῖς]. These words, as they stand, make no sense. Schneider sought a solution of the difficulty in Pliny's paraphrase (xxxiii. 114): 'optimum uero supra Ephesum Cilbianis agris harena cocci colorem habente'. He argued that μικρὸν was a repetition of μικρὸν following ὑπὲρ 'Εφέσου above, and that ἐν καλοῖς was a corrupt reading for ἐν ἀγροῖς Κιλβιανοῖς. But ἀγροῖς is a mere latinism; and a reading to be preferred, not only for this reason, but also because it is closer to that of the manuscripts, is ἐν Κιλβιανοῖς, which was suggested independently by Walter Leaf (*Journal of Hellenic Studies*, xxxvi (1916), footnote to p. 15). The manuscripts of the *De Lapidibus* are erratic in their treatment of place-names. The Cilbian Plain was a short distance to the east of Ephesus (Strabo xiii. 1. 13). For the Cilbiani, the inhabitants of this district, see A. H. M. Jones, *The Greek City* (Oxford, 1940), pp. 66–67.

πλύνουσι καὶ τρίβουσιν is a case of *hysteron proteron*, as is shown by τρίψαντες . . . πλύνουσιν above.

ἀλλὰ πλύσματι ⟨τῷ⟩ ἐπάνω χρῶνται ἓν πρὸς ἓν ἀλείφοντες. Schneider writes: 'fateor . . . me non intelligere'; and Wimmer's rendering 'sed lotura summa utuntur, unum alteri illinentes' is not enlightening. The translation given by Caley and Richards is 'separate portions are wetted one after the other'. ἓν πρὸς ἕν, however, must mean 'above all', a sense acquired from its use in comparisons. Cf. Plato, *Laws* 738e and *Epinomis* 976e, with E. B. England's notes on *Laws* 705b and 738e. The literal translation is: 'However, they use the washings on top above all for distempering.' For ἀλείφειν meaning

'to distemper', lit. 'to bedaub', cf. Herodotus iii. 8, ἀλείφει τῷ αἵματι
. . . λίθους ἕπτα, and Thucydides iii. 20, ἐξαληλιμμένον, 'completely
whitewashed'. The 'washings' could not be used for the painting of
pictures, the purpose which Theophrastus has primarily in mind
during his discussion of the earths. See §§ 50, 51 (end), 62, and 67.

§ 59. ἐκ τῶν ἀργυρείων, i.e. the silver-mines of Laurium. The approximate date of the invention is 405 B.C. (see below). This was the year
preceding the fall of Athens and the end of the Peloponnesian War.
Callias had no doubt rented a holding in the Laurium mines, but after
the Spartan occupation of Decelea in 412 B.C., mining operations
ceased (Thucydides vi. 91 and vii. 27). As a result, Callias must have
migrated to Asia Minor, hoping to repair his fortunes by striking gold
in the river valleys (οἰόμενος ἔχειν τὴν ἄμμον χρυσίον). Instead of gold
he discovered a source of cinnabar far closer to Greece than any previously known.

J. Kirchner, *Prosopographia Attica* (Berlin, 1901), vol. i, p. 521, suggests that this Callias may be none other than Socrates' wealthy friend
Callias, the son of Hipponicus. This is most unlikely. A well-known
noble such as he would have been described not as 'Callias, an (or the)
Athenian from the silver mines', but as 'Callias the son of Hipponicus',
or simply as 'Callias'.

χρυσίον. Here and in § 26 the word is virtually equivalent to χρυσός.
Cf. [Aristotle] *De Mir. Aus.* 833ᵃ30 and 833ᵇ (4 times).

ἐπραγματεύετο καὶ συνέλεγεν, i.e. 'collected and studied', a case of
hysteron proteron; cf. § 48, ⟨ἅμα⟩ τοῖς χυτοῖς καὶ ὀρυκτοῖς, and the note
ad loc.

περὶ ἔτη μάλιστ' ἐνενήκοντα εἰς ἄρχοντα Πραξίβουλον Ἀθήνησι.
Praxibulus was archon in 315 B.C. (Olympiad 116. 2, see Diodorus
Siculus xix. 56). The *De Lapidibus* must therefore have been written
in 315 B.C. or a little later. (The question is discussed more fully on
pp. 8–12.) For the phrase, cf. *H.P.* 6. 3. 3, οἰκοῦσι δὲ μάλιστα περὶ τριακόσια (sc. ἔτη) εἰς Σιμωνίδην ἄρχοντα Ἀθήνησιν, 'the men of Cyrene
have been living there for some three hundred years, reckoning to the
archonship of Simonides at Athens'. As Simonides was archon in 310
B.C., Theophrastus reckoned that Cyrene had been founded about
610 B.C. Similarly, according to him, the manufacture of artificial
cinnabar was invented approximately ninety years before 315 B.C.,
that is, about 405 B.C.

The passage is open to misinterpretation. For example, Hill translates: 'And this is no old Thing, the Invention being only of about
Ninety years Date; Praxibulus being at this Time in the Govern-
ment of Athens.' Hill clearly did not know the date of Praxibulus'

archonship. A similar misunderstanding has led L. Thorndike to favour 225–224 B.C. as the date of the *De Lapidibus* ('Disputed Dates, Civilization and Climate, and Traces of Magic' in the Scientific Treatises ascribed to Theophrastus, in *Essays on the History of Medicine*, edited by Charles Singer and Henry E. Sigerist, London, 1924, pp. 72–73). According to this interpretation, we should have to assign the foundation of Cyrene to 10 B.C.

§ 60. μιμεῖται τὴν φύσιν ἡ τέχνη. Art imitates Nature in the sense that artificial processes seek to reproduce the results of natural processes. White lead (§ 56), verdigris (§ 57), and cinnabar (§ 58) are all produced artificially by processes which 'imitate' natural processes of 'separation' (ἔκκρισις: see § 2). This is especially evident in the case of cinnabar: see p. 24. Similarly fire is assumed to play virtually the same part in the production of artificial ruddle as in that of natural ruddle (§ 54). The phrase has the same force in Arist. *Mete.* 381ᵇ8.

φαντασίας here means 'appearance'. Cf. *C.P.* 2. 16. 5, ἔοικεν . . . κατὰ φαντασίαν ἡ μεταβολὴ γίνεσθαι, and [Arist.] *De Coloribus* 2, φαντασίαν ποιεῖ μέλανος.

τὰς ἀλοιφάς, 'wall-paint'. Cf. Plato, *Crit.* 116b, χαλκῷ περιελάμβανον πάντα τὸν περίδρομον, οἷον ἀλοιφῇ προσχρώμενοι. See also the note on ἀλείφειν in § 58 (end).

ὅταν κιννάβαρι τριφθῇ. See the critical apparatus. κιννάβαρι corresponds to 'minium' in Pliny's paraphrase (xxxiii. 123): 'fit autem duobus modis: aereis mortariis pistillisque trito minio, &c'. τί was presumably a stopgap, like μέν in §§ 55 and 69. Quicksilver can be obtained by this means, but the process is tedious and the result an amalgam of mercury and copper.

λάβοι here and in § 40 means 'find'. Cf. *H.P.* 6. 1. 2, μεγίστην δ' ἄν τις λάβοι διαφοράν. *De Lap.*, § 50, εἴη δ' ἂν λαμβάνειν καὶ ταύτας τὰς διαφοράς is probably similar.

CHAPTER IX

§ 61. τὰ ἐν τοῖς γεωφανέσιν. These earths (mostly clays) are extracted from 'earth-pits', of which they are the sole products, unlike ruddle, ochre, &c., which are usually mined in association with metalliferous ores (§§ 50–52). τὸ γεωφανές does not appear to occur elsewhere in this sense, but γεωφανεῖον and γεωφάνιον are found in the lexicographers. See Pollux vii. 99 and the *Etymologicum Magnum*, s.v. γεωφανεῖον (χωρίον ἐστίν, ἐν ᾧ γῆς εἶναι μέταλλον).

ὥσπερ ἐλέχθη κατ' ἀρχάς. There is no suggestion in the introduction that this group of earths 'is generated from a "conflux" or "secretion" more pure and uniform than the others'. See p. 15 with n. 1. This passage is discussed on pp. 22–23 and 24, n. 2.

τῶν ὑποκειμένων here apparently means no more than 'materials'. Cf. *De Igne* 36, ἔχει δὲ καὶ πρὸς τὰς τήξεις καὶ πρὸς τὰς ἑψήσεις . . . μεγάλας ἕκαστα τὰ ὑποκείμενα διαφοράς.

ἐξ ὧν. As the antecedent supply ἐκ τούτων with λαμβάνουσι. The reference is to the earths considered in this chapter.

τὰς μὲν . . . τὰς δὲ . . . could be taken to refer proleptically to the stones from Asia (τὰς λίθους κτλ.). But the Greek is more natural and the sense more satisfactory if these words are linked with what immediately precedes, ἐξ ὧν κτλ. The noun to be supplied will then be 'earths', and the phrase will describe the treatment given to various earths in manufacturing the 'stones', which are possibly glazed bricks (cf. § 48 and note). Theophrastus follows the normal practice of not using γῆ in the plural. In the next sentence, at the beginning of § 62, the definite article is used in the feminine plural with the same reference to 'earths' (αἱ δ' αὐτοφυεῖς κτλ.). Elsewhere, in §§ 50–51, Theophrastus uses the neuter plural for this purpose (ἔνια, πάντα). If Theophrastus is referring to glazed bricks from Mesopotamia or Iran τήκοντες καὶ τρίβοντες will refer to the manufacture of the glazes, and μαλάττοντες to the 'puddling' of the clay for the bricks themselves.

τήκοντες καὶ τρίβοντες is a case of *hysteron proteron*, to which πυροῦντες καὶ μαλάττοντες (§ 48) is a close parallel.

τὰς ἐκ τῆς Ἀσίας ταύτας. For ταύτας see § 41, ἡ μαγνῆτις αὕτη λίθος.

§ 62. ἥ τε Μηλιὰς, κτλ. Melian earth is described in this section, the Samian in this section and in § 63, and the Tymphaic or 'gypsum' in §§ 64–end. Cimolian earth is not mentioned again (but see the note on the beginning of § 64). Melian earth is the white silica 'Milowite', or kaolin, or a natural mixture of the two; Samian earth is a very white, dense kaolin; the Cimolian is a fuller's earth consisting essentially of calcium montmorillonite.

τὸ γὰρ ἠρέμα τραχῶδες. See the critical apparatus. Smoothness (λειότης, in the preceding sentence) is one of the defects of Samian earth. 'Moderate roughness' in the Melian earth will provide a suitable contrast.

⟨ἅμα⟩ τῷ ψαφαρῷ. See the critical apparatus. 'Loose, crumbling texture' suggests a contrast with the 'solidity' (πυκνότης) of the Samian earth. The comparison is completed by τὸ . . . ἀλιπές and τὸ λίπος ἔχειν.

§ 63. ἡλίκον δίπους. See the critical apparatus. ἡλίκον must be read since its use here corresponds to that of ὅσον in qualifying numbers and numerical epithets. ἡλίκη would be possible only if a noun followed. See § 47, ὅσον διπλασία.

διαφυὴν . . . ἀστήρ. See the critical apparatus. The first seam (διαφυή) was of better quality than the earth at the extremities of the vein (τῶν ἔξω). It is safe to assume that the last seam was the best of all since it had a special trade-name, 'Star', and was perhaps stamped with a star as a guarantee of its quality. We may compare the Lemnian earth, of which a special kind carried a stamp representing a goat (Dioscorides v. 97, Wellmann), this stamp being 'sacred to Artemis' (Galen xii, p. 170, Kühn).

The description of the vein. Although in certain respects the description is obscure, it enables us to visualize adequately the geological formation of the site. The vein (φλέψ), we are told, extended for a considerable distance: this no doubt refers to its longitudinal dimensions. The strata above and below were of rock (ἐφ᾽ ἑκάτερα δ᾽ αὐτὴν λίθοι περιέχουσιν), and the height of the vein was approximately 2 feet (ἡλίκον δίπους). Hence it was impossible for the miners to stand upright (οὐκ ἔστιν ὀρθὸν στῆναι) at the face.

The two dimensions so far given, considerable length and a height of 2 feet, provide no difficulty. The third dimension given is a *depth* of considerably more than 2 feet (τὸ δὲ βάθος πολλῷ μείζων). If we had been told that the vein was considerably more than 2 feet in *breadth*, this would have been easily intelligible. But could the vein have had both *height* and *depth*? There is no reason to suspect the text at this point, and only one interpretation is possible. The height (ὕψος) must be the real height ('true thickness') of the vein, as shown by a line bisecting it perpendicularly, while the depth (βάθος) must be the apparent height ('apparent thickness'), expressed by a vertical line forming part of the radius of the earth's circumference. If the vein were horizontal, its real height and apparent height would be equal (see Fig. 1). But since in the present case the apparent height exceeds the real height, it is clear that the vein must dip at an angle (see Fig. 2).

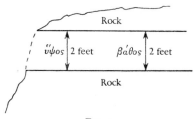

FIG. 1

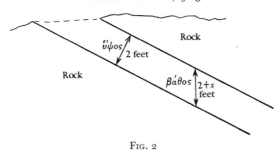

FIG. 2

Finally, we learn that the vein had running through the middle (διὰ μέσου) a seam (διαφυήν) superior in quality to the outer portions of the vein (βελτίων . . . τῶν ἔξω). There were also a second and a third seam, and lastly a fourth, the quality of which was the best of all (reading βελτίστη δ' ἡ ἐσχάτη). These four seams must have been thin layers running through the vein (see Fig. 3), so that this part of the paragraph must be a description of a vertical cross-section of the vein.

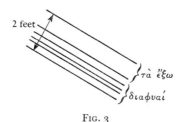

FIG. 3

Working from the top, we first have several inches of inferior material, below which at the middle of the vein runs the first good seam. The lower half of the vein contains a second and a third seam of similar quality (reading ἑτέραν τοιαύτην), and a fourth, yielding the best earth. Below this seam there was possibly a layer of the same inferior quality as that which formed the upper part of the vein above the seams. This must be the case if the term τὰ ἔξω, 'the outer portions', applies both to the top and to the bottom of the vein. If, however, there was such a layer, it must have been much thinner than the top layer (see Fig. 3).

Although Theophrastus implies that this Samian pit shaft was exceptionally small, it was in all probability not much smaller than most mining galleries of the same period. At Laurium few galleries were larger than 3 feet by 2½ feet (K. D. White, 'The Birth of Mining', *Optima*, v (1955), 4, p. 118).

§ 64. **χρῶνται δὲ τῇ γῇ . . . ἢ μόνον.** For Samian earth, see the Commentary on § 62. For μάλιστ᾽ ἢ μόνον de Laet, followed by Hill, reads μάλιστα τῇ Κιμωλίᾳ, so as to include a further reference to Cimolian earth in the text. There is no justification for this reading.

οἱ περὶ Θετταλίαν. See the critical apparatus. Perrhaebia was a district of northern Thessaly, and Tymphaea a neighbouring district of northern Epirus. The usual reading, οἱ περὶ τὸν Ἄθων, is unsatisfactory, if only because Mt. Athos is more than 100 miles away from Tymphaea. The gypsum of these districts and of Cyprus is the natural mineral, while that of Phoenicia, Syria, and Thurii in south Italy is plaster of Paris produced by heating the mineral (see § 69).

§ 65. For **ἀλαβαστρίτης** (onyx marble), see § 6.

χρῶνται γὰρ . . . κολλῆσαι. See the critical apparatus. Lit. 'They use it both for buildings, pouring (it) round the stone itself, and also if they wish to cement anything else of the same kind (sc. as a building).' The reference is to grouting with a plaster of Paris slurry, not to bonding with a lime mortar, as Caley and Richards (op. cit., p. 215) suppose.

§ 66. **ἡ δὲ οὐδαμῶς ἀνίησι.** See the critical apparatus. For a similar instance of an apodotic δέ, see Arist. *Mete.* 383ᵃ29 ff., ὅσα δὲ διὰ ψῦξιν καὶ τοῦ θερμοῦ συνεξατμίσαντος (sc. πήγνυται), ταῦτα δ᾽ ἄλυτα . . . ἀλλὰ μαλάττεται.

§ 67. **εἰς τὸν οἶνον.** Plaster of Paris is still added to the crushed grapes in the production of 'flor' sherry. Hill reads εἰς τὴν κονίασιν, for 'whitewash', but this emendation is less close to the manuscript reading, εἰς τὸν οἰκεῖον.

τὰ ἀπομάγματα, 'seal impressions'; cf. *C.P.* 6. 19. 4, καθάπερ τὰ ἀπομάγματα τῶν δακτυλίων.

§ 68. **τὰ τῆς κονίας.** Here κονία means 'quicklime': see § 9 and the note. Here, as in § 66, the thermal reaction is exaggerated.

For ἤδη, 'on occasion', cf. Aelian, *De Natura Animalium* iv. 32, ἤδη δὲ καὶ ἵππων πλευραῖς ἐμπεσόντες διέσχισαν.

§ 69. **ποιοῦσι . . . καὶ καίοντες.** See the critical apparatus. καὶ καίοντες can be retained if ποιοῦσι is read for καίουσι. Cf. § 64, ἐν Φοινίκῃ δὲ καὶ ἐν Συρίᾳ καίοντες τοὺς λίθους ποιοῦσιν.

καίουσι δὲ μάλιστα . . . καίεσθαι καὶ μᾶλλον. The restoration of this passage must depend on Pliny's statement (xxxvi. 182): 'qui coquitur lapis non dissimilis alabastritae esse debet (cf. § 65) aut *marmoroso. in Syria durissimos ad id eligunt cocuntque cum fimo bubulo, ut celerius urantur.'*

1. Schneider's conjecture καὶ ἁπλῶς τοὺς στερεωτάτους neatly corrects καὶ ἁπλουστέρους, στερεωτάτους and gives satisfactory sense : 'they burn mostly limestone, and absolutely the hardest limestone at that'. For ἁπλῶς used thus with a superlative, cf. *C.P.* 2. 4. 9 and 3. 1. 6, ἁπλῶς γὰρ τὸ μέγιστον.

2. After στερεωτάτους Schneider, Wimmer, and Caley and Richards read μὲν παρατιθέντες ⟨βόλιτον ἔνεκα⟩ τοῦ θᾶττον κτλ. Here βόλιτον is amply justified by Pliny's 'cum fimo bubulo' and is also required by the next sentence, in which the choice of the fuel, whatever it is, is explained by the fact that it burns efficiently and economically. But in most of the manuscripts the lacuna before τα is very short and suggests that only the alteration of τα into ἔνεκα can be provided for at this point. Moreover, μέν is superfluous and βόλιτον should precede παρα-τιθέντες because it is the most emphatic word in the clause. This immediately leads to the conclusion that βόλιτον should take the place of μέν, which was probably written as a stopgap for a troublesome word, as in § 55. See the note on τὸν Σκύθην κύανον ad loc.

μαρμάρους. Plaster of Paris is not made from limestone or marble. Theophrastus probably mistook the character of Phoenician and Syrian gypsum pebbles and exaggerated their hardness.

δοκεῖ γὰρ θερμότατον . . . διαμένει. Caley and Richards (op. cit., pp. 60, 221) make this sentence refer to γύψος, which is feminine, whereas it should refer to a neuter word, βόλιτον, ox-dung, the fuel used for burning the gypsum. διαμένειν is similarly used of the lasting qualities of a *fuel* in § 12.

πυρώδης τις ἡ γένεσις. Because Theophrastus supposes that gypsum (like quicklime) possesses innate heat, he accordingly concludes that fire is the efficient cause of its generation. See p. 34. ἐκ τούτων has better manuscript authority than ἐκ τούτου and gives better sense. It refers to several pieces of 'evidence' given in §§ 66 and 68 by Theophrastus in support of his supposition. It has already been mentioned that Theophrastus exaggerates the thermal reaction of plaster of Paris.

SELECT BIBLIOGRAPHY

BOOKS

ADAMS, F. D., *The Birth and Development of the Geological Sciences*, Baltimore, 1938.

AGRICOLA, GEORGIUS, *De Re Metallica*, Basle, 1657.

—— *De Re Metallica*, translated by H. C. and L. H. Hoover, London, 1912.

ALEXANDER OF APHRODISIAS, *In Aristotelis Meteorologicorum Libros Commentaria*, ed. M. Hayduck, Berlin, 1899 (*Commentaria in Aristotelem Graeca*, vol. iii, pt. ii).

ARISTOTLE, *Meteorologica*, translated by E. W. Webster (in vol. iii of *The Works of Aristotle Translated into English*, ed. W. D. Ross), Oxford, 1923.

—— *Meteorologica*, text with translation by H. D. P. Lee (Loeb Classical Library), London, 1952.

—— *On Marvellous Things Heard (De Mirabilibus Auscultationibus)*, text with translation by W. S. Hett in *Minor Works* (Loeb Classical Library), London, 1936.

—— *Problems*, text with translation by W. S. Hett (Loeb Classical Library), 2 vols., London, 1936–7.

—— *Rhetoric*, commentary by E. M. Cope, revised and edited by J. E. Sandys, 3 vols., Cambridge, 1877.

ATHENAEUS, *Deipnosophistae*, text with translation by C. B. Gulick (Loeb Classical Library), 7 vols., London, 1927–41.

AVICENNA. *See* HOLMYARD, E. J.

BIGNONE, E., *L'Aristotele perduto*, 2 vols., Florence, 1936.

BOODT, A. DE, *Gemmarum et Lapidum Historia . . . Cui accedunt Ioannis de Laet . . . De Gemmis & Lapidibus libri II. Et Theophrasti liber De Lapidibus cum brevibus notis*, Leiden, 1647.

BUNT, C. G. E., '*Chaffers' Handbook to Hall Marks on Gold and Silver Plate*, 7th ed., London, 1945.

CALEY, E. R., and RICHARDS, J. F. C., *Theophrastus On Stones*, introduction, text, translation, and commentary, Columbus, Ohio, 1956.

DANA, E. S., *A System of Mineralogy*, New York, 6th ed., 1920; 7th ed., vol. i, 1944.

—— *A Textbook of Mineralogy*, 4th ed., New York, 1932.

DAVIES, OLIVER, *Roman Mines in Europe*, Oxford, 1935.

DIELS, H., *Fragmente der Vorsokratiker*, 3 vols., 7th ed., Berlin, 1954.

DIODORUS SICULUS, text with translation by C. H. Oldfather, &c. (Loeb Classical Library), 12 vols., London, 1933– .

DIOGENES LAERTIUS, text with translation by R. D. Hicks (Loeb Classical Library), 2 vols., London, 1925.

DIOSCORIDES, *De Materia Medica libri quinque*, ed. M. Wellmann, 3 vols., Berlin, 1906–14.

DÜRING, I., *Aristotle's Chemical Treatise, Meteorologica iv*, Göteborg, 1944.

FORBES, R. J., *Studies in Ancient Technology*, vol. vii (Ancient Geology), Leiden, 1963.

GALEN, *Opera omnia*, ed. C. G. Kühn, 20 vols., Leipzig, 1821–33.

GORRINGE, H. H., *Egyptian Obelisks*, London, 1885.

HOLMYARD, E. J., and MANDEVILLE, D. C., *Avicennae de Congelatione et Conglutinatione Lapidum*, Paris, 1927.

HOW, W. W., and WELLS, J., *A Commentary on Herodotus*, 2 vols., Oxford, 1912.

JAEGER, W., *Aristoteles*, Berlin, 1923.

—— *Diokles von Karystos*, Berlin, 1938.

KING, C. W., *The Natural History of Precious Stones and Gems*, 1st ed., London, 1865; 2nd ed., London, 1867.

LEAF, W., *Strabo on the Troad*, Cambridge, 1923.

LENZ, H. O., *Mineralogie der alten Griechen und Römer*, Gotha, 1861 (containing translated excerpts from the *De Lapidibus* with notes).

LIPPMANN, E. O. VON, *Entstehung und Ausbreitung der Alchemie*, vol. i, Berlin, 1919; vol. ii, Berlin, 1931.

LYELL, Sir CHARLES, *Principles of Geology*, London, 1872.

MÉLY, F. DE, *Les Lapidaires de l'Antiquité et du Moyen Age*, 3 vols., Paris, 1896–1902. (Vol. iii, pt. i, contains a translation of the *De Lapidibus* with a somewhat fanciful interpretation of the opening sections.)

MICHELL, H., *The Economics of Ancient Greece*, 2nd ed., Cambridge, 1957.

MIDDLETON, J. H., *The Engraved Gems of Classical Times*, Cambridge, 1891.

OLYMPIODORUS, *In Aristotelis Meteora Commentaria*, ed. W. Stüve, Berlin, 1900 (*Commentaria in Aristotelem Graeca*, vol. xii, pt. ii).

PAULY, A. F., WISSOWA, G., KROLL, W., WITTE, K., *Real-Encyclopädie der klassischen Altertumswissenschaft*, Stuttgart, 1893–(cited as 'Pauly–Wissowa').

PAUSANIAS, *Description of Greece*, translated with notes by J. G. Frazer, 6 vols., London, 1898.

PLINY, *Natural History*, text with translation by H. Rackham, &c. (Loeb Classical Library), 10 vols., London, 1942–63.

ROSE, V., *Aristoteles Pseudepigraphus*, Leipzig, 1863.

SCHWARZE, C. A., *De lapide Lydio commentatio*, pt. i, Görlitz, 1805; pt. ii, Görlitz, 1806.

SINGER, C., and SIGERIST, H. E., *Essays on the History of Medicine* (including one by L. Thorndike on disputed dates, &c., in Theophrastus), London 1924.

SMITH, G. F. H., *Gemstones*, 13th ed., revised by F. C. Phillips, London, 1958.

SOLMSEN, F., *Aristotle's System of the Physical World*, Cornell, 1960.

STEPHANIDES, M. K., *'Ορυκτολογία τοῦ Θεοφράστου*, Athens, 1896.

STRABO, text with translation by H. L. Jones (Loeb Classical Library), 8 vols., London, 1917–32.

TAYLOR, A. E., *Commentary on Plato's Timaeus*, Oxford, 1928.

THEOPHRASTUS, *Enquiry into Plants* (*Historia Plantarum*), text with translation by Sir Arthur Hort (Loeb Classical Library), 2 vols., London, 1916.

—— *Metaphysics*, ed. W. D. Ross and F. H. Fobes, Oxford, 1929.

—— *On Stones*, &c. See p. 51.

Usener, H., *Analecta Theophrastea*, Leipzig, 1858.

Vitruvius, *De Architectura*, text with translation by E. Granger (Loeb Classical Library), 2 vols., London, 1931–4.

Walters, H. B., *Catalogue of the Engraved Gems and Cameos, Greek, Etruscan, and Roman, in the British Museum*, London, 1926.

Watson, J., *British and Foreign Building Stones*, Cambridge, 1911.

—— *British and Foreign Marbles and Other Ornamental Stones*, Cambridge, 1916.

ARTICLES

Bromehead, C. E. N. (C. N.), 'Ancient Mining Processes', *Antiquity*, xvi (1942), 193–207.

—— 'Geology in Embryo', *Proc. Geol. Assoc.*, lvi (1945), 89–134.

—— 'Practical Geology in Ancient Britain', ibid. lviii (1947), 345–67; lix (1948), 65–76.

Eichholz, D. E., 'Theophrastus on ΠΟΡΟΣ, *Classical Review*, lviii (1944), 18.

—— 'A Curious Use of μέν', ibid., New Series, ii (1952), 144–5.

—— 'Theophrastus, ΠΕΡΙ ΛΙΘΩΝ 25', ibid. viii (1958), 221–2.

Gottschalk, H. B., 'The Authorship of *Meteorologica*, Book IV', *Classical Quarterly*, New Series, xi (1961), 67–79.

Hammer-Jensen, I., 'Das sogenannte IV. Buch der Meteorologie des Aristoteles', *Hermes*, l (1915), 113–36.

Laurie, A. P., 'Ancient Pigments', *Archaeologia*, lxiv (1913), 315–36.

Mieleitner, K., 'Zur Geschichte der Mineralogie', *Fortschr. Min. Kristall. und Petrographie*, vii (1922), 427–80 (containing a translation of Theophrastus *De Lapidibus*, 431–45).

Regenbogen, O., 'Eine Forschungsmethode antiker Wissenschaft', *Quellen und Studien zur Geschichte der Mathematik, Astronomie und Physik*, Series B, i, pt. ii (1931), 131–82.

—— 'Theophrast-Studien', *Hermes*, lxix (1934), I, pp. 75–105; I, 2, pp. 190–203.

—— 'Theophrastos', Pauly–Wissowa. Suppl. vii, s.v.

Richards, J. F. C., 'Heinsius and a Manuscript of Theophrastus', *Classical Philology*, liv (1959), 118–19.

—— 'Nine New Manuscripts of Theophrastus *On Stones*', ibid. lviii (1963), 34–36.

Ridgeway, W., 'How far could the Greeks determine the fineness of gold and silver coins?', *Numismatic Chronicle*, series 3, xv (1895), 104–9.

Robertson, R. H. S., 'Cimolian Earth', *Classical Review*, lxiii (1949), 14–16.

—— 'Melian Earth', ibid., New Series, viii (1958), 223.

—— ' "Perlite" and Palygorskite in Theophrastus', ibid. xiii (1963), 132.

Wellmann, M., 'Die Stein- und Gemmenbücher der Antike', *Quellen und Studien zur Geschichte der Naturwissenschaften und der Medizin*, iv, pt. 4 (1935), 86 ff.

Wray, D. A., 'Greece: its Geology and Mineral Resources', *Mining Magazine*, xl (1929), *passim*.

INDEX

I. ENGLISH WORDS AND PROPER NAMES

2. GREEK WORDS

ἀναθυμίασις, see exhalation.
ἀνδρείκελον, 76, 123.
ἀνθρακοῦσθαι, 60, 97.
ἄνθραξ, see anthrax.
ἀντιπάσχειν, 62, 98–99.
ἀπηθεῖν, 78, 125.
ἀπολιθοῦν, 58, 70, 91, 114.
ἀπολίθωσις, 35 n., 74, 122.
ἄπυρος, 78, 125.
ἄτοπος, 72, 116–17.
αὐτάρκης, 76, 124.

βασανίζειν, 58, 72, 91, 117.

γεωφανές, τό, 80, 128.

διάζωμα, 58, 93.
διαφανής, 70, 112–13.
διάφασις, 68.
διαφορά, 6, 56, 58, 64, 68, 72, 74, 80, 82, 90, 92, 116, 121.
διαφυή, 62, 130–1.
διήθησις, see filtering.
δοκιμάζειν, 72, 74.
δύναμις, 56, 58, 64, 72, 74, 84, 86–87, 90, 93, 94, 121.

ἐκκρίνεσθαι, 56, 87.
ἔκκρισις, see secretion, separation.
ἔκλευκος, 70, 114.
ἐκπορούσθαι, 60, 62, 97–98.
ἔμφασις, 68.
ἓν πρὸς ἕν, 80, 126.
ἐργασία (process of manufacture), 78, 81.
(working of stones), 58, 66, 72, 92; and see κατεργασία.
εὐμεγέθης, 70, 113.

θερμόν, τό, see heat.
θραυστός, 60, 96.

Ἰβηρία, 78, 135–6.
ἰδιότης, 56, 90.
ἰδιωτέρως, 66, 105.

καιόμενος ('volcanic'), 64, 101.
κατακτός, 60, 96.
κατεργασία, 68.
καῦσις, 56, 58, 91, 94.
κέραμος, 60, 95.
κονία, 34, 43–45, 47, 60, 76, 84, 95, 122, 132.

λαμβάνειν ('find'), 70, 74, 80, 114, 120, 128.
λείωμα, 78.
λιθοκόλλητα, τά, see inlay-work.
λίπος, see greasiness.

μάρμαρος, 30, 34, 60, 84, 95, 133.
μέν (as stopgap), 78 n., 84 n., 125, 133.
μεταβάλλειν, 72, 78, 117, 124.
μεταλλευόμενα, τά, 4, 56, 70, 86, 87, 121; and see metals.
μεταλλευτός, 4, 80, 121.

ξύλον, 67 n., 107.

ὀρυκτός, 4, 68, 70, 72, 74, 121; and see fossiles.
οὐκέτι ('not similarly'), 58, 93.

παράτριψις, 72, 118.
περιπλάττειν, 78, 124.
πῆξις, see solidification.
πύρωσις, 58, 60, 74, 91, 94, 122.

ῥάβδος, 25, 66, 76, 105–6, 123.

σημεῖον ('portent'), 74, 120.
('streak'), 74, 118.
σιδήριον, 58, 72, 116.
συρροή, see conflux.
σύστασις, 56, 88.
σχεδόν, 6, 58, 62, 70, 74, 80.

τέμνειν, see quarrying.
τῆξις, see dissolution.
τι (as stopgap), 80 n., 128.

ὕλη, 56; and see matter.
ὑποκείμενα, τά, 80, 129.

φαντασία, 80, 128.
φλέψ, 82, 130.
φυσικός, 78, 124.
φύσις ('a kind'), 66, 70, 76, 106.

χρυσίον, 66, 80, 106, 127.
χρυσόπαστος, 64, 102.
χυτός, 74, 78, 80, 121, 125.

ψῆφος, 74, 120.
ψῦξις, see refrigeration.
ψυχρόν, τό, see solidification by cold.

PRINTED IN GREAT BRITAIN
AT THE UNIVERSITY PRESS, OXFORD
BY VIVIAN RIDLER
PRINTER TO THE UNIVERSITY